28 Day Mediterranean Diet Plan

MOST RECIPES UNDER 10 MINUTES

GW00984837

PRESENTED BY:

Ayhan with Debra Grossano, MS, RD, CDN, CNE

AYHAN'S 28-DAY MEDITERRANEAN DIET PLAN®

DISCLAIMER

This book details the author's personal experiences with and opinions about health, wellness, fitness and longevity. The author is not a healthcare provider.

The author and publisher are providing this book and its contents on an "as is" basis and make no representations or warranties of any kind with respect to this book or its contents. The author and publisher disclaim all such representations and warranties, including for example warranties of merchantability and healthcare for a particular purpose. In addition, the author and publisher do not represent or warrant that the information accessible via this book is accurate, complete or current.

The statements made about products and services have not been evaluated by the U.S. Food and Drug Administration. They are not intended to diagnose, treat, cure, or prevent any condition or disease. Please consult with your own physician or healthcare specialist regarding the suggestions and recommendations made in this book.

Except as specifically stated in this book, neither the author or publisher, nor any authors, contributors, or other representatives will be liable for damages arising out of or in connection with the use of this book. This is a comprehensive limitation of liability that applies to all damages of any kind, including (without limitation) compensatory; direct, indirect or consequential damages; loss of data, income or profit; loss of or damage to property and claims of third parties.

You understand that this book is not intended as a substitute for consultation with a licensed healthcare practitioner, such as your physician. Before you begin any healthcare program, or change your lifestyle in anyway, you will consult your physician or other licensed healthcare practitioner to ensure that you are in good health and that the examples contained in this book will not harm you.

This book provides content related to topics physical and/or mental health issues. As such, use of this book implies your acceptance of this disclaimer.

Table of Contents

The Healthiest Diet in the World!

The Mediterranean diet has been hailed as "The World's Healthiest Diet!" Ayhan, founder of a leading restaurant group in New York for over 25 years, used his popular Mediterranean restaurant cuisine to create Ayhan's Mediterranean Menu Plans®, a healthy weight loss program. It combines delicious, healthy foods in the proper portions to ensure steady weight loss that stays off.

The recipes, founded on two thousand years of cuisine are made for quick, easy preparation using high quality ingredients. These award winning recipes have been analyzed and portion controlled by the nutritionist Debra Grossano. Now you can enjoy delicious meals that will help you lose weight and stay healthy, if you follow the plan's ingredients and the proper portions.

Mediterranean cuisine has many healthy foods. Debra enhanced this latent health factor by focusing each meal on balanced nutritional content and regulated portions. From wine for a healthy heart to whole grains, dry fruits and vegetables for its high fiber, each meal has been created to offer the high nutritional value in keeping with your individual weight loss goal.

Ayhan is originally from the island of Cyprus, and spent many years studying Mediterranean cuisine from Greece, Turkey, Lebanon, Israel and Sicily. He opened his first Mediterranean restaurant in Long Island over 25 years ago and now has the largest group of Mediterranean restaurants in New York. He used this knowledge and experience to create a well balanced, enjoyable, healthy diet that is proven to take off the weight for good. The many health benefits of the Mediterranean diet include helping to prevent heart attacks, reducing blood pressure, and assist in reducing the risk of breast and prostate cancer.

All of the recipes are created to provide an enjoyable balanced meal and the ingredients selected are intended to promote health and weight reduction in a harmonious blend. All the ingredients needed are easily available either online or at your local supermarket. From fresh vegetables and fish to wine, the recipes offer the delicious dining experiences prepared in a few minutes. The quality of easily prepared meals that are rich in flavor and use fresh ingredients is generally superior to most diet plans that use pre-packed or frozen meals.

Now you can **lose 10 pounds or more in a month** and keep that weight off. The "Anti-Aging" Maintenance plan used in conjunction with **Ayhan's Mediterranean Menu Plans®** will ensure you remain your target weight indefinitely.

The plan is intended to promote greater physical energy while reducing stress. Anti-aging and heart healthy ingredients found in the recipes, such as **Vitamin E** and **omega 3 fatty acids**, maximize these benefits. All of this while enjoying delicious, health conscious meals that can be made in minutes.

Lose weight and keep it off!

How would you like to lose 10 pounds per month and keep it off indefinitely? Now you can lose the weight and keep it off while enjoying a more active lifestyle. The benefits Mediterranean diet make Ayhan's Mediterranean Menu Plans® diet the best in the world.

"I lost 42 lbs with this cuisine."
— W.M., Randolph, NJ

There are so many diets out there today it can be overwhelming having to choose which one to use. The hundreds of diet books rarely match a person's specific individual needs and it is very difficult to cater many diets to any one person. Now it's easy. Ayhan's Mediterranean Menu Plans® offers a diet plan that will be tailored to your needs, while still offering astounding weight loss benefits. This customization is offered online is unique in the diet industry and separates Ayhan's Mediterranean Menu Plans weight loss program from the pack.

Some diets you can buy from the supermarket come prepackaged and might not meet your individual requirements, or make you feel satisfied. Ayhan's Mediterranean Menu Plans® diet combines high quality ingredients in moderate amounts so you can easily make delicious meals that are nutritionally balanced and tailored to your needs so you can shed pounds fast.

"I went from a size 14 to a **size 5"**

-Marisol, Uniondale, NY

"What's the best diet? No question, according to dozens of recent studies: the Mediterranean diet wins, hands down."
– USA Weekend

Ayhan's Mediterranean Menu Plans® weight loss recipes are derived from the award winning Ayhan's restaurants and cover the entire spectrum of Mediterranean cuisine, and many are available for free. You can check out the online recipes here. There are classic and grilled salad recipes that revolve around a variety of different salads. These are heavy in vegetables and light, healthy dressings with Vitamin E for anti-aging properties. Marinade recipes focus on the preparation and cooking of meats for a hearty meal of moderate size. The low-carb recipes offer delicious meals designed to limit carbohydrate intake. These are just a few of the recipes offered by Ayhan's Mediterranean Menu Plans® diet and by joining the My Mediterranean Club you can find many more and save on online food purchases.

A Healthy Body means Better Living

Most diets only look into devising ways to take weight off, but take little or no interest into your overall health. This can cause many health problems besides resulting in regaining all the weight the short term fix diet took off. Ayhan's Mediterranean Menu Plans® is balanced so that you will be able to lose weight and have more energy for your daily activities. There is no reason you need to feel tired or worn out from dieting. A healthy weight loss diet should make you feel better and full of vigor and that is exactly what Ayhan's Mediterranean Diet does for you.

The Mediterranean diet has a high proportion of fish, fruits and vegetables, and monounsaturated fats such as olive oil. It allows a low intake of meat and dairy products. This combination has been found in scientific studies to lower the risk of Alzheimer's by 40 percent over conventional diets.

"That is a pretty significant effect," said Dr. Nicolas Scarmeas, assistant professor of neurology at Columbia University Medical Center.
— Forbes

Many studies have indicated that the Mediterranean diet has shown conclusive evidence in helping prevent heart attacks and cardiovascular disease. High concentrations of omega 3 fatty acids found in fish, such as salmon and flounder, are ideal in helping reduce heart disorders. These same studies have proven that following the diet reduces high blood pressure and cholesterol. It has also been shown to help reduce the chance of ALS (Lou Gehrig Disease) and birth defects such as spina bifida. All of these heart benefits make the Mediterranean diet the smart choice for anyone looking for a healthy way to lose weight.

"The Mediterranean diet will prevent heart problems, also will help with post-surgery, and maintaining a healthy lifestyle. I highly recommend this diet to all my patients."
— Dr. Sinan Berkay, Heart Specialist, Long Island

Oleic acid found in olive oil has been conclusively linked to helping protect against cancer, including prostate and breast cancer. Olive oil is a principal ingredient in the Mediterranean diet and its cancer preventive properties offer a compelling argument for using the Mediterranean diet. Vitamin E is a proven anti-aging agent and is found in all Ayhan's Salad Dressings and Marinades. These affects are apparent in people of all ages, making the Mediterranean diet a great choice whether you are in your twenties, or eighties.

Researchers looked at people aged 70 to 90 for more than a decade, and found those who adhered to a healthy low-fat Mediterranean-style diet lowered their risk of death by 23 percent, reports The Early Show's Dr. Emily Senay.

These are just some of the many health benefits gained by using the Mediterranean diet. Other benefits include: reducing the risk of gallstones, hypertension, and metabolic syndrome, while increasing insulin protection and longevity. There is no reason why everyone cannot be enjoying healthier living while eating great and losing weight.

What makes the Mediterranean diet better than the rest?

The **Atkins Diet** has many disadvantages when matched up against Ayhan's Mediterranean Menu Plans® diet. An in-depth comparison reveals many flaws in the Atkins Diet and displays the balance and heart healthy benefits Ayhan's provides. Atkins is high in saturated fats, low in fiber and carbohydrates, while limiting the variety of foods you can eat, such as fruit. Ayhan's Mediterranean Menu Plans® diet has none of those deficiencies, helps you lose weight fast, and keeps you fit. It's a much healthier way to take off the weight and keep it off all while enjoying yummy food that's good for you.

Successful diets inevitably lead to spin-offs. One of these spin-offs of the Mediterranean diet is called the **South Beach Diet**. A highly popular diet, it still comes up short. Ayhan's Mediterranean Menu Plans® weight loss program is more comprehensive, convenient and less restrictive. A full comparison shows Ayhan's is more balanced and healthier, while the portion-control program devised by Debra Grossano is designed with long term weight loss in mind. Health problems can arise by constantly changing your diet. Ayhan's Mediterranean Menu Plans® is for life and this stability is another important advantage this brings to successfully maintaining a healthy body.

The **Sonoma Diet** is yet another weight loss program that is derived from the Mediterranean diet. However, it also does not match up to the quality of Ayhan's Mediterranean Menu Plans® weight loss program. The Sonoma Diet is highly regimented with three phases and is restrictive and expensive. The Sonoma Diet's first phase curtails the use of many healthy ingredients. This approach may provide short term weight loss, but it is counterproductive for long term results, and is expensive to boot. Ayhan's diet is consistent, easy to use, allows a wide variety of high quality food, and is designed to offer a well balanced daily meal plan. Comparing the Ayhan's Mediterranean to the Sonoma Diet readily shows the limitations of the Sonoma Diet and the wide range of advantages Ayhan's Mediterranean Diet secures.

Another aspect of Ayhan's Mediterranean Menu Plans® that separates it from many other diets is that it is completely customizable. Following instructions from a book limits the versatility of a diet.
Ayhan's Mediterranean Menu Plans® is available online and is fully customized to individual needs.

Ayhan's Mediterranean Menu Plans® vs. Atkins®

Ayhan's Mediterranean Menu Plans®	Atkins®
Balanced between protein, fat, carbs	High in fat and protein, low in carbs
High in healthy unsaturated (especially mono) fats	High in saturated, unhealthy fat
High in fiber which is beneficial to the heart and digestive system and can help prevent certain cancers	Low in fiber; low fiber diets have been linked to constipation, colon cancer, diverticulosis, breast cancer, prostate cancer
High in all fruits and vegetables	Limits fruits and vegetables
High in essential vitamins and minerals obtained only from carbs, fruits and vegetables	
High in calcium from low fat dairy	Low in calcium
Healthy, steady, and permanent weight loss	Short-term weight loss
	When carbs are re-introduced, weight gain occurs rapidly and typically weight exceeds the weight when a person was before the diet
Risk of constipation is low because of high fiber content	Can result in constipation
Allows moderate amount of wine, which has been shown to be heart healthy	Does not allow wine, which prevents a person from getting the heart healthy benefits from it
Life long eating style	Short term eating style; nearly impossible to eat low carb for a lifetime; drop out rate is high
	Can cause bad breath from ketosis (body uses fat as energy in the absence of carbohydrates)
High in phytochemicals ("disease fighting weapons") found only in fruits and vegetables	Low in phytochemicals
Allows for some sweets which helps prevent a feeling of deprivation, and subsequent binge eating	Can lead to cravings and binging b/c of deprivation
Ketosis does not occur	The process of using fat as energy in the absence of carbs can cause an increase in ketones and uric acid which can cause kidney problems, gout and headaches
An energizing diet that helps to improve exercise performance	Can decrease energy levels, resulting in poor exercise performance

Ayhan's Mediterranean Menu Plans® vs. South Beach®

SIMILARITIES	
Based on restaurant quality recipes.	Based on restaurant quality recipes.
Promotes healthy, monounsaturated fats.	Promotes healthy, monounsaturated fats.
Low in unhealthy, saturated fats that come from meats and cheeses.	Low in unhealthy, saturated fats that come from fatty meats and cheeses.
Online membership includes access to a nutritionist.	Online membership includes access to a nutritionist.

DIFFERENCES	
Promotes moderate intake of alcohol, especially wine.	Does not allow wine or alcohol in first phase of diet.
Provides a well balanced diet, with no restrictions.	Does not allow certain fruits and vegetables, such as, carrots, white potatoes, pineapple, banana, and watermelon, which each have their own nutritional benefits.
High in fiber.	High in fiber, only after the initial, very low carbohydrate phase.
You can order your foods for the diet directly online and have them shipped to your home.	No online food purchases can be made from the website.
All meals and snacks are portion controlled to ensure long term weight loss.	Does not promote portion control.
A diet that has been around for thousands of years and has been shown to increase longevity and decrease the risk of major diseases.	A new "fad" diet with no long term studies done.

Ayhan's Mediterranean Menu Plans® vs. The Sonoma Diet™

SIMILARITIES	
Promotes portion and calorie control.	Promotes portion and calorie control.
Believes food should be enjoyed and taste good.	Believes food should be enjoyed and taste good.
DIFFERENCES	
No phases. Consistent foods and consistent meal plan.	Has 3 distinct phases.
No restrictions on fruits and alcohol at any point. Expect consistent weight loss that will stay off.	Phase 1 is very restrictive, no fruits or alcohol, and results in rapid weight loss. Rapid weight loss is unhealthy and tends to result in rapid weight gain when the diet is not followed.
A realistic meal plan that is easy to follow at all times.	Phase 1 is difficult to follow and unrealistic.
Does not result in deprivation at any point of the meal plan.	People will likely want to remain in phase 1 of the diet because of the quick weight loss. However phase 1 is not well balanced and is a set up for deprivation and yo-yo weight loss.
Involves recipes that are easy and quick to make. Gives alternate cooking methods and ingredients that shorten time. Ingredients are affordable. A "no cook" meal plan is available.	Entire diet is based on complicated and time consuming recipes that require expensive ingredients.
A realistic meal plan that does not have unrealistic expectations. Promotes healthy foods, but understands that people cannot eat perfectly all of the time. All foods can fit into the meal plan.	The diet asks people to get rid of all food in their house containing refined flours, non whole grains, hydrogenated and saturated fats, sugars and any oil other than olive, nut or canola.
Foods can be purchased online or in any supermarket.	Recipes call for ingredients that may only be available in specialty stores.
Website has an entire section for exercise, including a fitness expert and access to fitness videos and information.	Briefly touches on exercise.

Mediterranean Diet Pyramid – The Key to Successful Dieting!

The Mediterranean Diet Pyramid has been designed by studying the eating tendencies of the people of the Mediterranean region. Amounts are non specific to indicate the variation in use between these ingredients, depending on many conditions. This general diagram shows the basic foundation Ayhan and Debra used to design a unique weight loss program catered to your desires while offering all the benefits of the Mediterranean diet.

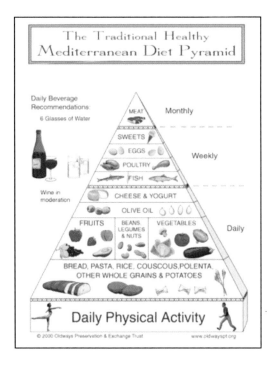

Food derived from plants naturally hold prominence in the diet and these include: fruits vegetables, potatoes, breads, grains, beans, nuts and seeds. An emphasis is placed on foods that require minimal processing andwhen possible are available locally. This helps maximize the health benefits of these foods. Olive oil is the principal supplier of fat intake in the Mediterranean diet and replaces other fats, such as butter, corn oil and margarine. This can seriously reduce saturated fat intake, with accompanying positive health & weight benefits.

Low to moderate amounts of cheese and yogurt may be served daily, though it is preferable to use low-fat to non-fat versions of these products. Moderate consumption of wine is allowed with meals. Recent studies have indicated the health benefits of moderate consumption of wine but it should be limited to one or two glasses a day (one for women).

In turn, a weekly allowance is made for low to moderate amounts of fish and poultry, and up to 4 eggs per week. Fish is favored over poultry for its health benefits. Red meat may be eaten in small amounts, though lean meats are favored for health factors. This wide ranging diet should be supplemented by regular physical activity to promote fitness.

Ayhan offers a wide range of products to be used in preparing Ayhan's Mediterranean Diet. These products are available online or at your local supermarket. There are a variety of All Natural diet products, low carb products, and prepared foods to go along with more conventional foods such as: dried fruit and snacks, nuts, kosher food, olives, grains, chocolates, and pastries. This short list goes a long way in showing the wide variety of food available in Ayhan's Mediterranean Menu Plans® Diet and proves you can enjoy fresh, wholesome meals and lose weight at the same time.

Taking it one week at a time

Ayhan's Mediterranean Menu Plans® is designed around a weekly regimen intended to meet the specific nutritional needs of the individual, while at the same time promoting weight loss. Each day offers well rounded meals and snacks with the opportunity for a wide variety of food to tempt your palate.

Many dieters find it difficult to stick to a diet since they offer a very limited range of food to eat. It is vital to stick to the weekly regimen, and by offering a wide range of recipes designed to provide the essential nutrients needed to support an active, fit lifestyle, each individual is able to create a plan that will meet their daily requirements with sumptuous meals suited to their particular tastes. Eating food you like creates an incentive to stick to the regimen and this is half the battle when looking to lose weight and keep it off.

The variety of food available for any dieter under Ayhan's Mediterranean Menu Plans'® weekly plan is readily apparent when looking at the following chart by clicking here.

The plan chart has dinners of spinach pie, shrimp kebabs, salmon, chicken kebabs, lamb chops, flounder and healthy Greek salad. This wide variety of food can tempt anyone and the best part is you will lose weight and feel better by eating such wonderful food!

The ability to design and quickly prepare great tasting, healthy meals in portions designed to maximize weight loss is what gives Ayhan's Mediterranean Menu Plans® diet no down side. The ability to work around your favorite Mediterranean ingredients makes the diet user friendly, and amenable to any palate. This flexibility is unparalleled in dieting and places Ayhan's Mediterranean Menu Plans® Weight Loss program head and shoulders above the competition.

Ayhan's Mediterranean Menu Plans® Week 1

Sunday
Nut Butter Breakfast
Babaganoush and Hummus Platter
Spinach Pie
Banana Shake

Monday
Cottage Cheese & Fruit
Hummus Sandwich
Side Salad/Oven Roasted Lamb Chop w/ Green Beans & Couscous
Orange Cream Smoothie

Tuesday
Yogurt Parfait
Lentil Soup
Shrimp Kebab with Basmati Rice and Steamed Vegetables
1 Apple/Side Salad

Wednesday
Honey Yogurt with Cottage Cheese
Mediterranean Spinach and Fig Salad
Quick Chicken Kebab Over Basmati Rice with Spinach
Banana Shake

Thursday
Fruit and Cheese Plate
Turkey and Fig Jam Sandwich
Quick Grilled or Baked Salmon/Grilled Zucchini
Hummus and Baby Carrots

Friday
Mediterranean Spinach and Olive Omelet
Healthy Greek Salad
Quick and Healthy Margherita Pizza/Sautéed Spinach
Banana and Nut Butter

Saturday
Tomato and Mushroom Frittata/Vanilla Milk
Taboule Salad
Flounder Marmaris
Cubed Fruit/Greek Yogurt and Cranberries

Quick and Easy Great Tasting Meals!

A diet is much easier to follow with delicious food to eat. You will have to be eating the food every day you might as well be able to enjoy it! That is the beauty behind Ayhan's Mediterranean Menu Plans® Diet, the food is great tasting and healthy! This feature supplementing the great weight loss results is what makes Ayhan's Mediterranean Menu Plans® weight loss program the best all around diet in the world.

In the hectic lifestyles most of us have, few of us have all the time in the world to prepare gourmet meals. Ayhan's Mediterranean Menu Plans® Diet is styled around the modern lifestyle and is intended to offer high quality meals in a limited amount of time. Most of the recipes are designed for less than 20 minutes of time spent in the kitchen preparing and cooking, many with less than ten! Fresh home cooked delicious meals that help you lose weight and maintain a healthy lifestyle. It sounds almost too good to be true but looking at a sample recipe will quickly convince you otherwise:

Sample Recipe - Salmon Delite (414 cals)

Ingredients

- 4 oz canned sockeye salmon
- 1 cup tomatoes, diced
- 1 cup cucumber, diced
- 1/2 cup green pepper, diced
- 1 tbsp parsley, chopped
- 1/4 cup low fat feta cheese, crumbled
- 3 tbsp Ayhan's Lite Mediterranean Vinaigrette Dressing and Marinade

Prep Time: 10 minutes
Total Time: 10 minutes

Combine all ingredients except salmon and toss with dressing.
Top mixture with salmon and serve.

A diet that provides a healthy, easily prepared meal, using fresh vegetables in 10 ten minutes is something you can't afford to ignore. A sampling of one day of a weekly regimen provides additional proof of the quick, easy delectable meals offered in Ayhan's Mediterranean Menu Plans® Diet. All of the meals are able to be made in 15 minutes or less and are portioned to give the proper amount of essential vitamins and minerals, such as Vitamin E and C, and Iron, along with limiting saturated fats and cholesterol. This healthy well balanced approach to designing meals can be substantially modified to suit any taste.

With this in mind, Ayhan's Mediterranean Menu Plans® Diet offers those who join My M Club the opportunity to evaluate the recipes from the award winning Ayhan restaurants. This allows Ayhan and Debra the chance to learn about your tastes and to design dynamic new tantalizing recipes from classic Mediterranean ingredients to diversify your dietary intake while exciting your taste buds.

Ayhan's 28 Day Meal Plan© Guidelines

Ayhan's 28 Day Meal Plan© is designed to provide approximately 1500 calories per day. Most people will lose about 10 pounds if they follow the plan with exact measurements of food, but if you currently weigh more than 200 pounds you should add one snack of approximately 200 calories (use snacks already within the meal plan or just add 1 1/2 ounces Ayhan's Famous trail mix a day). Be sure to include the following beverage directions in your plan:

BEVERAGE DIRECTIONS

The following beverages are unlimited:

- Seltzer water (regular or flavored)
- Diet or sugar free drinks (no more than 10 calories per serving)
    - diet soda
    - diet iced tea
    - Crystal Light
    - flavored water
- Coffee or tea without sugar
  (sugar substitute is ok; Sweet n Low, Equal, Splenda)
- Water

The following beverages can be substituted for a snack in Ayhan's 28 Day Meal Plan©. When substituting, replace the snack with a beverage that is approximately the same calorie amount:

- 6 ounce glass of red or white wine (3 or 4 times per week) = 130 calories
- 4 ounce glass of 100% fruit juice = 60 calories
- 8 ounce glass of 100% fruit juice = 120 calories
- 8 ounce glass of fat free milk = 90 calories
- 8 ounce glass of plain soy milk = 130 calories
- 8 ounce glass of lite soy milk = 100 calories

If you have any questions please email our Diet Plan Administrator at diet@ayhans.com.

We also welcome your comments and testimonials, and will reward before and after photos. We wish you much success with your program!

Ayhan & the Menu Plans Team

Definitions

Babaghanoush: Baba ganoush or Babaghanoush is the name of two popular Middle Eastern dishes made primarily of eggplant. The first version of babaghanoush is a salad made of grilled eggplant with finely diced onions, tomatoes and other vegetables blended with olive oil. The second version is a paste made of roast or grilled eggplant and tahini, a paste made from sesame seeds. Both can be eaten in a variety of ways, including as a dip with whole wheat bread or crackers, spread on pita, or added to other dishes.

Basmati Rice: The Hindi word basmati, means fragrant, and refers to the nutlike flavor and aroma of this small, but long grained rice. When cooked, basmati rice gives off a wonderful aroma that adds to the experience of eating it. It has been used in India and Pakistan for thousands of years and is excellent with curries. Several varieties are now grown in the U.S., such as Texmati and Kasmati.

Bulgur: Bulgur is a quick-cooking form of whole wheat that has been cleaned, parboiled, dried, ground into particles and sifted into distinct sizes. Often confused with cracked wheat, bulgur differs in that it has been pre-cooked. Bulgur is ready to eat with minimal cooking or, after soaking in water or broth, can be mixed with other ingredients without further cooking. Bulgur can be used in recipes calling for converted rice (and it's more nutritious than rice). Bulgur has a nut-like flavor and can be used in place of couscous and rice in most recipes.

Cholesterol: Cholesterol is a soft, waxy substance found in the bloodstream, cells, and foods, such as meat and dairy products. Most cholesterol in the body is not a product of what you eat, but, rather, is produced by the liver. Some cholesterol is necessary in our bodies, however too much in the bloodstream can be unhealthy, and lead to hardening of the arteries. When doctors talk to their patients about the health concerns of cholesterol, they are often referring to "bad cholesterol", or low-density lipoprotein (LDL).

Couscous: A food consisting of grains made from semolina which resembles tiny pellets of grain. In the United States couscous is known as a pasta (similar to pastina), however in most other countries it is treated more like a grain in its own right. Couscous is traditionally served under a meat or vegetable stew.

Falafel: Falafel is a fried ball or patty made from spiced fava beans and/or chickpeas. It can also be baked to make a healthier version. Dry mixes can be purchased in supermarkets or specialty stores. They are easy to make, usually just requiring water to be added and then cooked.

Fiber: Fiber is defined as material made by plants that is not digested by the human gastrointestinal tract. Fiber is classified as a carbohydrate, but provides no vitamins, minerals, or calories. Fiber is found in fruits, vegetables, and beans, as well as, oat, bran, and wheat products. Fiber can reduce cholesterol, aid in weight loss, stabilize blood sugar, keep the digestive tract healthy, and relieve constipation. It is recommended to have 25-30 grams of fiber a day.

Greek Style Yogurt: A plain yogurt made usually from cow's milk, but also comes in sheep and goat,s milk versions. It has a creamy, thick texture similar to sour cream. Its creaminess is a result of the straining process that removes excess liquid. Greek yogurts available in the US come in whole milk, low fat, and nonfat versions, as well as flavored varieties. Greek style yogurt contains healthy bacteria (probiotics) just the same as American yogurt.

Definitions, continued...

HDL: HDL is the "good" cholesterol. It has a useful effect in reducing tissue cholesterol and taking it back to the liver. HDL actually protects against atherosclerosis. An abnormally low HDL level 1(according to the NCEP, anything below 40 milligrams per deciliter) is considered a risk factor for coronary artery disease. Exercise and healthy unsaturated fats have been shown to increase HDL levels.

Hummus: a dip made of chickpea paste and tahini (sesame seed paste), with flavorings such as olive oil, garlic, lemon juice, and paprika. The dip is made by pureeing the chick peas with the olive oil and spices. Hummus is traditionally scooped up with pita bread, but is increasingly popular as a dip for tortilla chips.

Insulin: Insulin is a hormone that lowers the level of glucose (a type of sugar) in the blood. It is released by the pancreas when blood glucose goes up, such as after eating and helps the glucose enter the body's cells, where it can be used for energy or stored for future use. In diabetes, the pancreas doesn't make enough insulin or the body can't respond normally to the insulin that is made. This causes the glucose level in the blood to rise.

LDL: LDL cholesterol is known as the "bad" cholesterol, because excess LDL cholesterol tends to stick to artery walls, which can, in turn, lead to plaque buildup and coronary artery disease including a heart attack. The recommended LDL goal has been 130 mg/dl, but a new option has been recommended to lower the LDL to less than 100 mg/dl. A diet high in saturated and trans fat, and low in good unsaturated fat is linked to elevated LDL levels.

Metabolic Syndrome: (also known as syndrome X or the dysmetabolic syndrome) is a term used to designate a cluster of risk factors that come together in a single individual. The main features of metabolic syndrome include insulin resistance, hypertension (high blood pressure), cholesterol abnormalities, and an increased risk for clotting. Patients are most often overweight or obese. The Mediterranean diet has been shown to decrease the risk for metabolic syndrome.

Monounsaturated Fats: Monounsaturated fats are fatty acids that are naturally occurring in foods, such as, olive oil, canola oil, certain nuts, and canola oil. Monounsaturated fat has been shown to be protective against cardiovascular disease and is recommended in the diet. Olive oil, an excellent source of monounsaturated fat, is a main ingredient in the Mediterranean Diet.

Oleic Acid: A monounsaturated fatty acid present in canola, corn and, most of all, olive oil. High concentrations of it can lower blood levels of cholesterol. It is found in large amounts in the Mediterranean diet because of its large presence in olive oil.

Omega 3 fatty acids: Fatty acids are molecules found in the body and in food. Omega 3 fatty acids are considered "essential" fatty acids because the body cannot produce them and they must be obtained from food. Many studies have shown that they reduce the risk of coronary heart disease. They are primarily found in fatty fish. The Mediterranean Diet is high in omega 3 fatty acids.

Phytochemicals: Phytochemicals are nonnutritive plant chemicals that contain protective, disease-preventing compounds. They are found in fruits, vegetables, nuts, seeds, whole grains, flax, and garlic, just to name a few. Phytochemicals are associated with the prevention and/or treatment of cancer, diabetes, cardiovascular disease, and hypertension.

Definitions, continued...

Risotto: Risotto is a traditional Italian dish made rice. The most common types of rice used are Arborio, Carnaroli or Vialone Nano. It is made by briefly sautéing the rice in olive oil or butter (often with some onion), then adding stock a little at a time and stirring constantly until the rice absorbs the stock. It usually takes between 20 and 30 minutes of stirring. When it,s done, the rice is cooked through and bound in a wonderful creamy sauce that is made as the starch leaches out of the rice grains and combines with the stock.

Saturated Fats: Saturated fats are naturally found in foods, such as palm kernel oil, coconut oil, cottonseed oil, fatty meats (visible as the hardened white part), whole milk dairy products, and butter. They have been shown to increase the risk for cardiovascular disease. They should be avoided as much as possible. The Mediterranean Diet is low in saturated fat.

Stuffed grape leaves: (also known as Dolma) Stuffed grape leaves are a Middle Eastern dish. The grape leaves are stuffed with rice and vegetables, and generally served cold. Stuffing ingredients can vary depending on the region they originate from. Grape leaves can be purchased jarred and then stuffed at home, or can be purchased already prepared with the stuffing.

Tabouli: (or tabbouleh) is a Middle Eastern mezze (appetizer or small plate). Its primary ingredients are bulgur, parsley, tomato, scallion, and other herbs chopped with lemon juice and various seasonings, generally including black pepper and sometimes cinnamon and allspice.

Total Cholesterol: It is the combination of LDL, HDL and very low-density lipoproteins (VLDL cholesterol). The recommended goal is less than 200 mg/dL.

Trans Fats: A type of unsaturated fat that is primarily created by partial hydrogenation (chemical process) of plant oils and animal fat by the processed food industry. Large food manufacturers use them often in their products because of their long shelf life, small need for refrigeration, and desirable properties for baking. They are listed on food ingredients as partially hydrogenated oil. They are found in fast foods, snack foods, fried foods and baked goods. Trans fats should be completely avoided.

Triglycerides: Triglycerides are found in fats in food and also produced by the liver. Triglycerides circulate through the blood all of the time, but do not enter the vessels and clog the arteries. Normal triglyceride level is less than 150 mg/dL. If levels are high, saturated and trans fat intake should be limited, as well as sugars and refined carbohydrates (white flour), which can cause the liver to produce triglycerides.

Vitamin E: Tocopherol, or vitamin E, is a fat-soluble vitamin that is an important antioxidant. Some beneficial claims of vitamin E include: enhances the body's immune system, helps protect against cardiovascular disease, protects the body from pollutants, and helps prevent the formation of blood clots. Ayhan's Mediterranean Salad Dressing and Marinades are fortified with vitamin E.

Hints for Making our Plan Even Faster
MEATS

- Use pre-grilled chicken which can be purchased in most supermarket deli sections or use Perdue chicken short cuts (grilled).
- If a salad recipe calls for grilled chicken, you can use deli slice chicken or turkey.
- Morton's makes a healthy frozen grilled fish which you can use in place of any fish on our plan.
- Look in the freezer section for tuna and salmon burgers. They can easily be grilled up or baked in place of any fish we have on our plan.
- Our website sells canned salmon and packaged tuna, which can both be used in place of the fish on the plan.

GRAINS

- Purchase boil in a bag instant brown rice…cooks in just 10 minutes.
- Couscous is a very quick cooking grain. You can interchange your grains and use couscous for those days you don't have the time to cook a longer cooking grain, such as basmati rice.
- You can always replace the starch in a recipe (rice, pasta, couscous, beans) with a whole wheat pita.

VEGETABLES

- Uses bagged salad mixes and add the extras on yourself.
- Instead of grilling fresh vegetables, you can purchase frozen vegetables and microwave them for 2-3 minutes in a microwave safe container covered with plastic wrap.

MISCELLANEOUS

- If you don't mind leftovers, double or even triple the ingredients on recipes to make it last for a few days. If you don't want it the next day, put it in Tupperware and freeze it to make your own frozen meal.
- If you find a recipe on our plan that's fast and tastes great, don't hesitate to use it on other days, even if it's not designated for that day.
- When the plan calls for soup, instead of making it from scratch you can purchase a canned soup (i.e. lentil).
- When making the spinach pie, if you cannot find phyllo dough or find it difficult to work with, you can purchase pizza dough from either your local bakery or pizza shop, or in the freezer section of your supermarket.
- Remember that babaganoush and hummus are both sold in most grocery stores.

Low Sodium Options and Substitutions

How To Make Ayhan's Mediterranean Menu Plans® Low Sodium

If you have been instructed by your doctor to follow a low sodium diet due to a medical condition, please read the instructions below to decrease the sodium content in our Mediterranean meal plans

Foods/Ingredients to Omit	Substitutions
Salt	Herbs and spices- pepper, oregano, basil, garlic, garlic powder, onion powder, red pepper flakes, mint, dill, salt free seasonings, rosemary
Olives or Capers	Any fresh or frozen vegetables, or canned vegetables with "no sodium added" along with herbs and spices
Ayhans Salad Dressings and Marinades	Olive oil, vinegar, and no salt seasonings; Mrs. Dash Marinades
Seasoning packets in the couscous mixes	Any herb or spice above
Salted nuts or seeds	Unsalted nuts and seeds
Canned vegetables, beans or prepared foods	Canned vegetables and beans that say "no salt added", prepared canned foods that say "low sodium", or dried beans
Canned soups	Low sodium soups such as Healthy Request or Healthy Choice
Canned salmon or tuna fish	Rinse before using to get rid of some of the sodium.
Anchovies	Any grilled fish without salt.
Cheese (especially feta)	Low sodium cheese varieties, such as Alpine lace
Cottage Cheese	Low sodium cottage cheese
Peanut butter	Natural peanut butter
Deli turkey or ham	Low sodium deli turkey or ham
Crackers or Gold'N Krackle Baked Wheat Crisps (sold on website)	Unsalted crackers, Wasa crackers, or Plain Gold'N Krackle Crisps
Glenny's soy chips	Unsalted Glenny's soy chips or plain rice cakes
Jarred or canned pasta sauce	Sodium free canned tomatoes (crushed would work best) or fresh tomatoes diced and sautéed with garlic and olive oil.
Breadcrumbs or croutons	Use unseasoned, plain
Black Olive spread (sold on website)	Homemade eggplant spread. Bake eggplant for 20-25 minutes and remove skin. Cut into cubes and sauté with olive oil, garlic and pepper. Cook until very soft. Blend in food processor.
Hummus	Homemade, salt free hummus. Using a food processor, blend chick peas (canned without added salt), garlic, fresh lemon juice, and tahini.
Packaged grilled chicken (Perdue chicken short cuts)	Rotisserie chicken, without any sauce (take the skin off).
Parmesan cheese	Salt free spices and herbs
Near East Falafel mix	Homemade falafel made without salt

Ayhan's
Mediterranean Menu Plans®

Week 1

Day 1 Meal Plan and Recipes

Breakfast   Nut Butter Breakfast (319 cals)
Prep time: 3 minutes   **Total time:** 3 minutes
Ingredients
 * 1 slice whole grain bread, toasted
 * 1 tbsp all natural nut butter (peanut, almond or cashew)
 * 2 tbsp **Ayhan's Famous Golden Raisins**
 * 1 cup non-fat milk, to drink
Directions: Spread nut butter on toasted bread and sprinkle raisins on top. Serve with glass of milk.

Nutrition Facts	
Calories	319
Total Fat	10g
Saturated Fat	2g
Cholesterol	4mg
Sodium	295mg
Total Carbs	48g
Dietary Fiber	5g
Sugars	29g
Protein	15g

Lunch   Babaganoush and Hummus Platter (573 cals)
Prep Time: 5 minutes   **Total Time:** 5 minutes
Ingredients
 * 1/3 cup babaganoush   * 1/3 cup hummus
 * 1/2 whole wheat pita/1 whole mini pita/pita chips
 * 1 cup salad greens   * 1/2 cup baby carrots   * 1/2 large cucumber, sliced
Directions:
Arrange babaganoush, hummus, and greens on a plate. Heat 1/2 whole pita in the oven for about 2 minutes, until crisp. Use cucumbers, baby carrots and crispy pita bread to dip.

Nutrition Facts	
Calories	573
Total Fat	22g
Saturated Fat	2g
Cholesterol	0mg
Sodium	530mg
Total Carbs	62g
Dietary Fiber	11g
Sugars	11g
Protein	22g

Dinner   Spinach Pie (466 cals)
Prep Time: 10 minutes   **Cook Time:**   15 minutes
Temperature Instructions: Preheat oven to 450 degrees
Ingredients
 * 2 cup spinach (frozen)   * 2 sheets phyllo dough   * cooking spray
 * 1 clove garlic, crushed   * salt and pepper to taste   * 2 tbsp **olive oil**
 * 1 tbsp parmesan cheese   * 2 egg whites   * 1/4 cup onions, diced
 * 2 ounce low-fat feta cheese
Directions: Steam the spinach either in the microwave or on the stovetop, squeeze out any water, and set aside. Sauté onions and garlic with 1 tbsp olive oil until soft. Add spinach and sauté 5 minutes. Allow to cool. Add cheeses, egg whites, and salt and pepper, to taste. Brush phyllo dough with remaining oil. Spread ingredients between 2 pieces of phyllo and fold into triangular shape. Spray cooking sheet with cooking spray to avoid sticking. Bake at 450 degrees for 10 minutes, until golden brown.

Nutrition Facts	
Calories	466
Total Fat	33g
Saturated Fat	5g
Cholesterol	15mg
Sodium	360mg
Total Carbs	26g
Dietary Fiber	2g
Sugars	7g
Protein	20g

Snack   Banana Shake (143 cals)
Prep Time: 5 minutes   **Total Time:** 5 minutes
Ingredients
 * 1 banana   * 1 packet sugar substitute
 * 1 cup non-fat milk   * 2 cups ice   * 1 tsp vanilla extract
Directions: Place all ingredients in blender, fill with 2 cups ice, and blend to desired consistency.

Nutrition Facts	
Calories	143
Total Fat	1g
Saturated Fat	0g
Cholesterol	4mg
Sodium	127mg
Total Carbs	26g
Dietary Fiber	1g
Sugars	23g
Protein	9g

Day 2 Meal Plan and Recipes

Breakfast — Cottage Cheese & Fruit (193 cals)
Prep time: 3 minutes   **Total time:** 3 minutes
Ingredients
   * 1/2 cup lite canned fruit (or 1 piece fresh fruit)
   * 2/3 cup nonfat cottage cheese
   * 6 **Ayhan's Famous Almonds**
Directions: Top Cottage cheese with fruit and nuts

Nutrition Facts	
Calories	193
Total Fat	4g
Saturated Fat	1g
Cholesterol	7mg
Sodium	20mg
Total Carbs	21g
Dietary Fiber	2g
Sugars	19g
Protein	19g

Lunch — Hummus Sandwich (298 cals)
Prep Time: 5 minutes   **Total Time:** 5 minutes
Ingredients
   * 1/3 cup hummus   * 1/2 cup tomatoes, sliced   * 1 cup nonfat milk
   * 1/2 whole wheat pita   * 1/2 cup cucumber, sliced   * 1/2 cup lettuce, sliced
Directions:
Hummus is a puree of chick peas (garbanzo beans) Open pita and spread hummus on inside. Stuff with lettuce, tomato, and cucumber. Serve with 1 cup milk.

Nutrition Facts	
Calories	298
Total Fat	9g
Saturated Fat	2g
Cholesterol	5mg
Sodium	565mg
Total Carbs	41g
Dietary Fiber	8g
Sugars	13g
Protein	18g

Dinner — Side Salad (64 cals)
Prep Time: 2 minutes   **Cook Time:**   2 minutes
Ingredients
   * 1 cup salad greens
   * 1 tsp **Ayhan's Lemon & Herb Dressing** or **Mediterranean Vinaigrette**
Directions: Toss salad greens with dressing and enjoy.

Nutrition Facts	
Calories	64
Total Fat	6g
Total Carbs	2g

Dinner — Oven Roasted Lamb Chop with Green Beans and Couscous (594 cals)
Cook Time: 20 minutes   **Total Time:**   20 minutes
Preheat oven to 450 degrees
Ingredients
   * 4 ounces lamb chop   * 1 cup fresh green beans (or 1 cup frozen)
   * 3 tbsp **Ayhan's Lemon & Herb Dressing and Marinade**
   * 2/3 cup cooked couscous, no added oil
Directions: Baste lamb chop with dressing and roast in the oven for 5 minutes on each side. Prepare couscous as directed on box, omitting added fat. Steam or microwave green beans until desired tenderness. Measure out 2/3 cup couscous onto a serving plate. Place lamb chop on top of couscous and arrange green beans around the plate.

Nutrition Facts	
Calories	594
Total Fat	36g
Saturated Fat	10g
Cholesterol	72mg
Sodium	583mg
Total Carbs	12g
Dietary Fiber	5g
Sugars	3g
Protein	25g

Snack — Orange Cream Smoothie (158 cals)
Prep Time: 5 minutes   **Total Time:** 5 minutes
Ingredients
   * 1 orange   * 1 tsp vanilla extract   * 2 cups ice
   * 1 cup non-fat milk   * sugar substitute if desired
Directions: Place all ingredients in blender, fill w/ 2 cups ice, & blend to desired consistency.

Nutrition Facts	
Calories	158
Total Fat	1g
Total Carbs	27g

Snack — Trail Mix (173 cals)
Prep Time: 1 minutes   **Total Time:** 1 minutes
Ingredients: 1/4 cup **Ayhan's Famous Berry Nutty Trail Mix** or **Hiker's Trail Mix**

Nutrition Facts	
Calories	173
Total Fat	11g
Total Carbs	17g

Ayhan's Lamb Chops with Red Peppers, Peas & Rice

Day 3 Meal Plan and Recipes

Breakfast — Yogurt Parfait (280 cals)
Prep time: 5 minutes   **Total time:** 5 minutes
Ingredients
* 1/2 cup bran cereal
* 1-6 ounce container nonfat Greek yogurt or nonfat light/plain yogurt
* 4 **Ayhan's Famous dried apricots** cut into small pieces
* 6 **chopped almonds** or 1/4 cup roasted nuts, chopped
Directions: In a tall glass, place a bottom layer of yogurt, a layer of apricots, and a layer of bran cereal, then repeat. Top parfait with chopped nuts.

Nutrition Facts
Calories	280
Total Fat	5g
Saturated Fat	0g
Cholesterol	7mg
Sodium	283mg
Total Carbs	57g
Dietary Fiber	15g
Sugars	28g
Protein	15g

Lunch — Lentil Soup (Each serving = 250 cals)
Prep Time: 5 minutes   **Cook Time**: 35 minutes   **Total Time:** 40 minutes
Ingredients
* 1 1/2 cup **red lentils**   * 2 tbsp **olive oil**   * 1/4 cup chopped onions
* 8 cups chicken/vegetable broth   * 1 peeled carrot, chopped   * pepper to taste
Directions: Add olive oil to a soup pot and sauté onions and carrots until tender. Rinse the lentils. Add lentils and broth to the soup pot and bring to a boil. Reduce the heat to a simmer. Cover pot halfway to allow steam to get out. Let simmer until lentils are soft, about 30 minutes. **Divide into 6 servings, about 1 cup per serving.**

Nutrition Facts
Calories	250
Total Fat	7g
Saturated Fat	1g
Cholesterol	0mg
Sodium	1986mg
Total Carbs	34g
Dietary Fiber	6g
Sugars	14g
Protein	14g

Snack — Side Salad (64 cals)
Prep Time: 2 minutes   **Total Time:** 2 minutes
Ingredients
* 1 cup salad greens
* 1 tbsp **Ayhan's Lemon & Herb Dressing** or **Mediterranean Vinaigrette**
Directions: Toss salad greens with dressing and enjoy.

Nutrition Facts
Calories	64
Total Fat	6g
Total Carbs	2g

Dinner — Shrimp Kebab with Basmati Rice and Steamed Vegetables (629 cals)
Prep Time: 5 minutes   **Cook Time**: 15 minutes   **Total Time:** 20 minutes
Temperature Instructions: Preheat oven to 450 degrees
Ingredients
* 4 oz shrimp, peeled & de-veined   * 4 1" thick onion slices   * 1 tsp margarine
* 4 tbsp **Ayhan's Lemon & Herb Dressing**   * 2/3 cup cooked **basmati rice**
* 4 grape tomatoes   * 4 whole mushrooms   * 1 c fresh/ frozen veggies
Directions: Mix shrimp, tomatoes, mushrooms, onions, with Ayhan's Lemon and Herb Dressing. Put them on skewers with one of each. Use second skewer if needed. Preheat oven to 500 and bake for 15 minutes. Meantime prepare basmati rice according to box. Serve shrimp and veggie kebab over basmati rice pilaf. Serve kebabs over rice and arrange vegetables around the plate.

Nutrition Facts
Calories	629
Total Fat	32g
Saturated Fat	5g
Cholesterol	172mg
Sodium	1151mg
Total Carbs	56g
Dietary Fiber	10g
Sugars	9g
Protein	34g

Snack — 1 Apple (81 cals)
Snack — Berry Smoothie (120 cals)
Prep Time: 5 minutes   **Total Time:** 5 minutes
Ingredients
* 1 c nonfat milk   * ¾ c. mixed berries (frozen)   * 1 packet sugar substitute
* 2 cups ice
Directions: Place ingredients in blender, fillw/ ice, & blend to desired consistency.

Nutrition Facts
Calories	120
Total Fat	1g
Total Carbs	20g

Ayhan's Shrimp Kebab over Rice

Day 4 Meal Plan and Recipes

Breakfast — Honey Yogurt w/ Cottage Cheese (190 cals)

Prep time: 3 minutes   **Total time:** 3 minutes

Ingredients
* ¼ cup nonfat cottage cheese   * 1 tbsp honey
* 1-6 ounce container nonfat Greek yogurt or nonfat light/plain yogurt

Directions: Mix honey into yogurt and spoon onto cottage cheese

Nutrition Facts	
Calories	190
Total Fat	0g
Saturated Fat	0g
Cholesterol	4mg
Sodium	117mg
Total Carbs	11g
Dietary Fiber	0g
Sugars	10g
Protein	8g

Lunch — Mediterranean Spinach and Fig Salad (565 cals)

Prep Time: 10 minutes   **Total Time:** 10 minutes

Ingredients
* 3 cups baby leaf spinach, raw   * 2 **organic Turkish figs**, sliced
* 1/2 cup canned chick peas (drained and rinsed) * 1 Kirby cucumber, sliced
* 4 **Ayhan's Famous walnut halves**   * 5 grape tomatoes
* 4 tbsp **Ayhan's Lite Mediterranean Vinaigrette Dressing and Marinade**

Directions: Toss all ingredients and enjoy.

Nutrition Facts	
Calories	565
Total Fat	19g
Saturated Fat	3g
Cholesterol	0mg
Sodium	2330mg
Total Carbs	74g
Dietary Fiber	23g
Sugars	23g
Protein	27g

Dinner — Quick Chicken Kebab Over Basmati Rice with Spinach (596 cals)

Prep Time: 5 minutes   **Cook Time:** 15 minutes   **Total Time:** 20 minutes

Temperature Instructions: Preheat oven to 450 degrees

Ingredients
* 4 ounces chicken breast (cubed)   * 4 small mushrooms   * 2 tsp margarine
* 4 tbsp **Ayhan's Lemon & Herb Dressing**   * 4 1" square pieces of onion
* 4 grape tomatoes   * 2/3 cup cooked **basmati rice**   * 2 cups fresh spinach

Directions: Cut chicken breast into 1" cubes. Baste with Ayhan's Lemon & Herb Dressing and arrange chicken, mushrooms, onions, and plum tomato on skewer (use vegetables to fill skewer) Bake in oven for 5 minutes. For Basmati Rice: Prepare as directed on package without added fat and melt margarine into rice after cooked. For Steamed Spinach: Use 2 cups fresh spinach or one cup frozen. Place in covered pot, without any added water. Steam until spinach cooks down.

Nutrition Facts	
Calories	596
Total Fat	29g
Saturated Fat	4g
Cholesterol	66mg
Sodium	896mg
Total Carbs	52g
Dietary Fiber	6g
Sugars	12g
Protein	35g

Snack — Banana Shake (143 cals)

Prep Time: 5 minutes   **Total Time:** 5 minutes

Ingredients
* 1 banana
* 1/2 cup nonfat milk
* 1/3 cup nonfat Greek yogurt or nonfat light/plain yogurt
* 1 packet sugar substitute
* 2 cups ice

Directions: Place all ingredients in blender, fill with 2 cups ice, and blend to desired consistency.

Nutrition Facts	
Calories	143
Total Fat	1g
Saturated Fat	0g
Cholesterol	4mg
Sodium	127mg
Total Carbs	26g
Dietary Fiber	1g
Sugars	23g
Protein	9g

Ayhan's Chicken Kebab over Rice

Day 5 Meal Plan and Recipes

Breakfast — Fruit and Cheese Plate (179 cals)
Prep time: 5 minutes   **Total time:** 5 minutes
Ingredients
* 1 cup cubes melon or choice of fruit   * 1 ounce low-fat cheese, diced
* 1 glass non-fat milk, to drink
Directions: Mix melon and cheese and enjoy.

Nutrition Facts

Calories	179
Total Fat	3g
Saturated Fat	2g
Cholesterol	11mg
Sodium	321mg
Total Carbs	23g
Dietary Fiber	1g
Sugars	21g
Protein	17g

Lunch — Turkey and Fig Jam Sandwich (226 cals)
Prep Time: 5 minutes   **Total Time:** 5 minutes
Ingredients
* 2 ounces fresh roasted turkey   * 2 tsp **Turkish fig jam**
* 1 piece whole wheat pita bread
Directions: Spread pita with fig jam and stuff with turkey.

Nutrition Facts

Calories	226
Total Fat	4g
Saturated Fat	1g
Cholesterol	54mg
Sodium	197mg
Total Carbs	29g
Dietary Fiber	2g
Sugars	10g
Protein	19g

Dinner — Quick Grilled or Baked Salmon (438 cals)
Prep Time: 2 minutes   **Cook Time:** 10 minutes   **Total Time:** 12 minutes
Temperature Instructions: Preheat oven to 450 degrees
Ingredients
* 3 ounces salmon filet   * 1/4 lemon   * 2/3 cup cooked **couscous**
* 3 tbsp **Ayhan's Lemon & Herb Dressing** * salt and pepper, to taste
Directions: Place fresh filet of Salmon in frying pan. Squeeze lemon over it and pour Ayhan's Lemon and Herb dressing over it. Sauté 5 minutes each side, if grilling 5 minutes each side, if baking, 8 minutes each side. While cooking salmon, boil water for couscous & prepare according to box directions. Serve couscous as a side dish.

Nutrition Facts

Calories	438
Total Fat	27g
Saturated Fat	5g
Cholesterol	50mg
Sodium	445mg
Total Carbs	26g
Dietary Fiber	1g
Sugars	1g
Protein	21g

Dinner — Grilled Zucchini (147 cals)
Prep Time: 1 minutes   **Cook Time:** 4 minutes   **Total Time:** 5 minutes
Temperature Instructions: Preheat oven to 450 degrees
Ingredients
* 1 zucchini   * 1 tbsp olive oil

Nutrition Facts

Calories	147
Total Fat	14g
Total Carbs	6g

Snack — Hummus and Baby Carrots (304 cals)
Prep Time: 2 minutes   **Total Time:** 2 minutes
Ingredients
* 1/3 cup hummus   * 1 cup baby carrots   * ½ cup fat free or soy milk
Directions: Dip baby carrots in hummus and serve with milk.

Nutrition Facts

Calories	304
Total Fat	10g
Total Carbs	41g

Snack — Papaya Yogurt (150 cals)
Prep Time: 2 minutes   **Total Time:** 2 minutes
Ingredients
* 6 oz nonfat Greek, light or plain yogurt   * ¼ c **Ayhan's Famous dried papaya**
Directions: Top yogurt with papaya chunks and enjoy.

Nutrition Facts

Calories	150
Total Fat	1g
Total Carbs	27g

Ayhan's Grilled Salmon

Day 6 Meal Plan and Recipes

Breakfast — Mediterranean Spinach & Olive Omellete (392 cals)

Prep time: 5 minutes **Cook Time:** 5 minutes **Total time:** 10 minutes

Ingredients
* 4 egg whites
* 8 **black olives**, sliced
* 1 tsp olive oil
* 1/2 cup baby spinach leaves
* 1 cup nonfat milk
* 1 cup melon, cubed
* 1/2 whole wheat pita, toasted or 1 mini whole wheat pita, toasted

Directions: Mix egg whites, spinach, and olives in a bowl. Heat 1 tsp olive oil in skillet and pour egg mixture in. Cook until eggs set and then flip. Serve the omellete with 1/2 whole wheat pita, milk, and melon cubes.

Nutrition Facts

Calories	392
Total Fat	10g
Saturated Fat	2g
Cholesterol	5mg
Sodium	786mg
Total Carbs	50g
Dietary Fiber	7g
Sugars	26g
Protein	31g

Lunch — Healthy Greek Salad (385 cals)

Prep Time: 10 minutes **Total Time:** 10 minutes

Ingredients
* 2 cups romaine lettuce
* 1/2 cup shredded carrot
* 1/2 celery stalk, diced
* 1/4 cup shredded red cabbage (or bagged coleslaw mix)
* 4 grape tomatoes
* 1/4 cup dill, chopped
* 1/2 cup chick peas
* 8 **black olives**
* 2 oz crumbled, low-fat feta cheese
* 4 tbsp **Ayhan's Mediterranean Vinaigrette Dressing and Marinade**

Directions: Toss all ingredients and enjoy.

Nutrition Facts

Calories	385
Total Fat	20g
Saturated Fat	3g
Cholesterol	10mg
Sodium	872mg
Total Carbs	41g
Dietary Fiber	12g
Sugars	10g
Protein	17g

Dinner — Quick and Healthy Margherita Pizza (244 cals)

Prep Time: 2 minutes **Cook Time:** 5 minutes **Total Time:** 7 minutes

Temperature Instructions: Preheat oven to 450 degrees

Ingredients
* 1 whole wheat pita
* 1/4 tsp garlic powder
* 4 slices of tomatoes
* 2 ounces low-fat shredded mozzarella
* to taste salt and pepper

Directions: Open pita bread and toast until slightly crispy in toaster oven, approximately 2 minutes. Spread slices of tomatoes on surface of pita and sprinkle with shredded cheese and garlic powder. Place back in the toaster oven and heat until cheese is melted, about 3 minutes. Add salt and pepper to taste.

Nutrition Facts

Calories	244
Total Fat	9g
Saturated Fat	5g
Cholesterol	34mg
Sodium	459mg
Total Carbs	19g
Dietary Fiber	3g
Sugars	3g
Protein	21g

Dinner — Sautéed Spinach (138 cals)

Prep Time: 1 minutes **Cook Time:** 5 minutes **Total Time:** 6 minutes

Ingredients
* 2 cups spinach, fresh
* 1 tbsp olive oil
* ½ clove garlic, crushed

Directions: Heat olive oil. Add garlic and sauté until golden brown. Add spinach and cook for 4 minutes on a low to medium heat to avoid burning.

Nutrition Facts

Calories	138
Total Fat	14g
Total Carbs	3g

Snack — Banana and Nut Butter (241 cals)

Prep Time: 2 minutes **Total Time:** 2 minutes

Ingredients
* 1 banana
* 1 tbsp nut butter
* 1 cup fat free or soy milk

Directions: Spread nut butter on banana and enjoy.

Nutrition Facts

Calories	241
Total Fat	10g
Total Carbs	29g

Snack — Sorbet and Berries (106 cals)

Prep Time: 2 minutes **Total Time:** 2 minutes

Ingredients
* ½ cup sorbet
* 2/3 cup fresh berries or choice of diced fruit

Directions: Top sorbet with sliced, fresh berries.

Nutrition Facts

Calories	106
Total Fat	0g
Total Carbs	26g

Ayhan's Greek Salad

Day 7 Meal Plan and Recipes

Breakfast   Tomato and Mushroom Frittata (233 cals)
Prep time: 5 minutes   **Cook Time:** 5 minutes   **Total time:** 10 minutes
Temperature Instructions: Preheat oven to 450 degrees
Ingredients
   * 4 egg whites   * 1 garlic clove   * 2 tsp olive oil   * salt and pepper, to taste
   * 1/2 cup diced tomato   * 1 scallion, chopped   * 1/2 cup sliced mushrooms
Directions: Mix all ingredients. Pre-heat frying pan and sauté mixture until egg is cooked through.

Nutrition Facts	
Calories	233
Total Fat	11g
Saturated Fat	1g
Cholesterol	0mg
Sodium	594mg
Total Carbs	19g
Dietary Fiber	6g
Sugars	8g
Protein	20g

Breakfast   Vanilla Milk (84 cals)
Prep time: 3 minutes   **Total time:** 3 minutes
Ingredients   * ½ tsp vanilla extract   * 1 cup nonfat milk
       * 1 packet sugar substitute   * cinnamon
Directions: Heat milk until warm. Mix vanilla, sugar substitute, cinnamon and sprinkle on top.

Nutrition Facts	
Calories	84
Total Fat	0g
Total Carbs	11g

Lunch   Taboule Salad (488 cals)
Prep Time: 10 minutes **Cook Time:** 25 minutes **Total Time:** 40 minutes
Ingredients
   *1 c. **Near East Taboule**, prepared according to directions or 1 c. cooked bulgur
   *1 diced tomato   * 3 tbsp **Ayhan's Famous Lemon & Herb Dressing**
   * tomato and cucumber slices (to garnish)   * 1 cup greens
   * 1 warm mini whole wheat pita, or regular sized whole wheat pita
Directions: Mix 1 cup of prepared taboule with diced tomato and Lemon & Herb Dressing and refrigerate for 30 minutes. Place on bed of greens and garnish with tomato and cucumber. Serve with heated pita. (If bulgur is used, season with salt, pepper, and 1/4 tsp dried mint.)

Nutrition Facts	
Calories	488
Total Fat	20g
Saturated Fat	3g
Cholesterol	0mg
Sodium	626mg
Total Carbs	69g
Dietary Fiber	19g
Sugars	16g
Protein	17g

Dinner   Flounder Marmaris (345 cals)
Prep Time: 5 minutes   **Cook Time**: 10 minutes   **Total Time:** 15 minutes
Temperature Instructions: Preheat oven to 450 degrees
Ingredients
   * 3 ounces filet of flounder   * 1 ounce sun dried tomatoes, diced   * 1 tbsp water
   * 1/2 tsp tomato paste   * 1 tsp dill, chopped   * 1 clove garlic, crushed
   * 2 tbsp **Ayhan's Lemon & Herb Dressing** * 1/2 cup tomatoes, diced
Directions: Place flounder in casserole or baking pan. In a separate bowl, mix all other ingredients. Pour the mixture over the flounder and bake for about 15 minutes.

Nutrition Facts	
Calories	345
Total Fat	15g
Saturated Fat	3g
Cholesterol	41mg
Sodium	1525mg
Total Carbs	35g
Dietary Fiber	0g
Sugars	12g
Protein	25g

Dinner   Bean Salad (254 cals)
Prep Time: 5 minutes   **Total Time:** 5 minutes
Ingredients   * 1/2 c. canned kidney beans, drained   * 1/4 cup diced red onion
   * 2 Tbl. **Ayhan's Lite Vinaigrette**   * salt & pepper   * 1/4 cup tomatoes diced
Directions: Mix all ingredients, chill and serve.

Nutrition Facts	
Calories	138
Total Fat	14g
Total Carbs	3g

Snack   Cubed Fruit (60 cals)
Prep Time: 2 minutes   **Total Time:** 2 minutes
Ingredients: 1 cup assorted fruit, cubes (or a single serving fruit cup in natural juice)

Nutrition Facts	
Calories	60
Total Fat	0g
Total Carbs	19g

Snack   Greek Yogurt and Cranberries (103 cals)
Prep Time: 2 minutes   **Total Time:** 2 minutes
Ingredients
   * ½ cup **Ayhan's Famous dried cranberries**   * 1 6 oz. container of nonfat Greek yogurt

Nutrition Facts	
Calories	103
Total Fat	0g
Total Carbs	18g

Ayhan's
Mediterranean Menu
Plans®

Week 2

Day 8 Meal Plan and Recipes

Breakfast — Nut Butter Breakfast (319 cals)

Prep time: 3 minutes   **Total time:** 3 minutes

Ingredients
* 1 slice whole grain bread, toasted   * 1 cup non-fat milk
* 1 tbsp all natural nut butter (peanut, almond, or cashew)
* 2 tbsp **Ayhan's Famous golden raisins**

Directions: Spread nut butter on toasted bread and sprinkle raisins on top. Serve with glass of milk.

Nutrition Facts	
Calories	319
Total Fat	10g
Saturated Fat	2g
Cholesterol	4mg
Sodium	295mg
Total Carbs	48g
Dietary Fiber	5g
Sugars	29g
Protein	15g

Lunch — Babaganoush and Hummus Platter (573 cals)

Prep Time: 5 minutes   **Total Time:** 5 minutes

Ingredients
* 1/2 cup babaganoush (purchase pre-prepared from grocery store)
* 1 cup salad greens   * 1/2 cup baby carrots
* 1/2 cup hummus (purchase pre-prepared from grocery store)
* 1/2 cucumber, sliced   * 1/2 whole wheat pita, (or 1 mini pita), warm

Directions: Arrange hummus, babaganoush, and greens on a platter. Warm 1/2 pita bread in the oven for about 2 minutes, or until crispy. Use pita, cucumber, and carrots to dip.

Nutrition Facts	
Calories	573
Total Fat	22g
Saturated Fat	2g
Cholesterol	0mg
Sodium	530mg
Total Carbs	62g
Dietary Fiber	11g
Sugars	11g
Protein	22g

Dinner — Spinach Pie (466 cals)

Prep Time: 10 minutes   **Cook Time:** 15 minutes   **Total Time:** 25 minutes

Temperature Instructions: Preheat oven to 450 degrees

Ingredients
* 1/4 cup fresh or frozen spinach   * 1/4 cup diced onions   * 2 tbsp olive oil
* 2 ounces low-fat feta cheese, crumbled   * 1 tbsp parmesan cheese, grated
* 1/4 tsp black pepper   * 2 sheets phyllo dough   * cooking spray
* to taste salt and pepper   * 2 egg whites   * 1 clove garlic, crushed

Directions: Steam the spinach either in the microwave or on the stovetop, squeeze out any water, and set aside. Sauté onions and garlic with 1 tbsp olive oil until soft. Add spinach and sauté 5 minutes. Allow to cool. Add cheeses, egg whites, and salt and pepper, to taste. Brush phyllo dough with remaining oil. Spread ingredients between 2 pieces of phyllo and fold into triangular shape. Spray cooking sheet with cooking spray to avoid sticking. Bake at 450 degrees for 10 minutes, until golden brown.

Nutrition Facts	
Calories	466
Total Fat	33g
Saturated Fat	5g
Cholesterol	15mg
Sodium	360mg
Total Carbs	28g
Dietary Fiber	2g
Sugars	7g
Protein	20g

Snack — Banana Shake (142 cals)

Prep Time: 5 minutes   **Total Time:** 5 minutes

Ingredients
* 1 banana   * 1 tsp vanilla extract
* 1 packet sugar substitute   * 2 cups ice
* 1 cup non-fat milk

Directions: Place all ingredients in blender, fill with 2 cups ice, and blend to desired consistency.

Nutrition Facts	
Calories	143
Total Fat	1g
Saturated Fat	0g
Cholesterol	4mg
Sodium	127mg
Total Carbs	26g
Dietary Fiber	1g
Sugars	23g
Protein	9g

Day 9 Meal Plan and Recipes

Breakfast — Cereal with Sliced Banana (342 cals)

Prep time: 2 minutes   **Total time:** 2 minutes

Ingredients
* 3/4 cup wheat or bran cereal
* 1 cup non-fat milk
* 1/2 banana, sliced
* 6 **Ayhans Famous Almonds**

Directions: Mix cereal in bowl with almonds, top with sliced banana, and finish with milk..

Nutrition Facts	
Calories	342
Total Fat	10g
Saturated Fat	2g
Cholesterol	4mg
Sodium	295mg
Total Carbs	48g
Dietary Fiber	5g
Sugars	15g
Protein	17g

Lunch — Grilled Chicken Shepherd Salad (407 cals)

Prep Time: 5 minutes   **Cook Time:** 5 minutes   **Total Time:** 10 minutes

Temperature Instructions: Preheat oven to 450 degrees

Ingredients
* 2 cups ripe tomato, diced
* 1 cucumber
* ½ cup red onions, diced
* 1 ounce low-fat feta cheese, crumbled
* 1/3 bunch dill, chopped diced
* 2 ounce grilled chicken breast, diced
* 3 tbsp **Ayhan's Mediterranean Vinaigrette Dressing and Marinade**

Directions: Grill chicken breast at 450 degrees for about 5 minutes and set aside to cool. Toss all ingredients and serve.

Nutrition Facts	
Calories	407
Total Fat	14g
Saturated Fat	3g
Cholesterol	78mg
Sodium	662mg
Total Carbs	35g
Dietary Fiber	9g
Sugars	22g
Protein	38g

Dinner — Scallops Mediterranean (577 cals)

Prep Time: 5 minutes   **Cook Time:** 15 minutes   **Total Time:** 20 minutes

Temperature Instructions: Preheat oven to 450 degrees

Ingredients
* 3 ounces sea or bay scallops
* 1 ounce sun dried tomatoes, diced
* 1/2 tsp tomato paste
* 2 tsp dill, chopped
* 2 tsp garlic, diced
* 1 cup rice pilaf, cooked
* 4 tbsp water
* 3 tbsp **Ayhan's Lemon & Herb Dressing and Marinade**

Directions: Place scallops in casserole or baking pan. In separate bowl, mix tomato paste with remaining ingredients (except rice). Pour mixture over scallops and bake at 450 degrees until tender, about 10 minutes. Prepare rice according to package directions, without adding any oil or butter. Place scallops over rice and drizzle remaining liquid over the top.

Nutrition Facts	
Calories	577
Total Fat	22g
Saturated Fat	4g
Cholesterol	28mg
Sodium	1139mg
Total Carbs	74g
Dietary Fiber	9g
Sugars	7g
Protein	1g

Dinner — Side Salad (64 cals)

Prep Time: 2 minutes   **Total Time:** 2 minutes

Ingredients
* 1 cup salad greens
* 1 tbsp **Ayhan's Lemon & Herb Dressing** or **Mediterranean Vinaigrette**

Directions: Toss salad greens with dressing and enjoy.

Nutrition Facts	
Calories	64
Total Fat	6g
Total Carbs	2g

Snack — Hazelnut Fruit Yogurt (180 cals)

Prep Time: 3 minutes   **Total Time:** 3 minutes

Ingredients
* 6 oz nonfat Greek yogurt
* 5 roasted hazelnuts
* 1 oz **Ayhan's Famous dried fruit** (3-4 pcs)

Directions: Top yogurt with roasted hazelnuts and dried fruit.

Nutrition Facts	
Calories	180
Total Fat	4g
Total Carbs	26g

Snack — 2 Tangerines (62 cals)

Prep Time: 1 minute   **Total Time:** 1 minute

Ingredients
* 2 tangerines (or 1 orange)

Ayhan's Scallops with Mushrooms, Peas and Rice

Day 10 Meal Plan and Recipes

Breakfast Nutty Honey Yogurt (370 cals)

Prep time: 3 minutes   **Total time:** 3 minutes

Ingredients
* 6 ounce container nonfat Greek yogurt, light yogurt or, nonfat plain yogurt
* 1 tbsp honey   * 6 **Ayhan's Famous roasted almonds**
* 1 ounce **Ayhan's Famous dried fruit of choice** (3-4 pieces)

Directions: Top yogurt with almonds and dried fruit. Drizzle honey on top.

Nutrition Facts	
Calories	370
Total Fat	9g
Saturated Fat	4g
Cholesterol	21mg
Sodium	113mg
Total Carbs	66g
Dietary Fiber	5g
Sugars	59g
Protein	10g

Lunch Sicilian Antipasto Salad (370 cals)

Prep Time: 10 minutes **Total Time:** 10 minutes

Temperature Instructions: Preheat oven to 450 degrees

Ingredients
* 2 cups greens   * 2 tomatoes, cut into wedges   * 3 oz tuna fish packed in water
* 1/4 cup **artichoke hearts**   * 3 radishes, sliced   * 8 **black olives**
* 1/2 red pepper, sliced   * 1/2 stalk of celery, chopped
* 1 tbsp parsley   * 1 tbsp capers   * 4 tbsp **Ayhan's Lite Vinaigrette**

Directions: Toss all ingredients and serve.

Nutrition Facts	
Calories	370
Total Fat	23g
Saturated Fat	3g
Cholesterol	0mg
Sodium	1420mg
Total Carbs	18g
Dietary Fiber	5g
Sugars	6g
Protein	27g

Dinner Tilapia over Asparagus Basmati Rice Pilaf (495 cals)

Prep Time: 5 minutes   **Cook Time**: 15 minutes   **Total Time:** 20 minutes

Temperature Instructions: Preheat oven to 450 degrees

Ingredients
* 3 ounces tilapia fish filet   * 1 cup **basmati rice**, cooked   * 1/4 cup onion, diced
* 1 tsp olive oil   * 2 tbsp **Ayhan's Lemon & Herb Dressing and Marinade**
* 4 spears asparagus, cut into 1" pieces   * 1/4 cup water
* 1/4 cup fennel, diced   * salt and pepper to taste

Directions: Prepare rice according to directions on package, without any added butter or oil, measure out 1 cup cooked, and set aside. Place tilapia in a casserole dish with a thin layer of water on bottom and bake for 5 minutes. Heat 1 tsp olive oil in saucepan. Sauté onions, asparagus and fennel until tender. Mix into cooked rice, along with lemon and herb dressing. Place fish on top of rice, add salt and pepper to taste.

Nutrition Facts	
Calories	495
Total Fat	18g
Saturated Fat	3g
Cholesterol	41mg
Sodium	353mg
Total Carbs	84g
Dietary Fiber	6g
Sugars	13g
Protein	29g

Snack Fruit n' Nut Frozen Yogurt (217 cals)

Prep Time: 5 minutes   **Total Time:** 5 minutes

Ingredients
* ½ cup nonfat frozen yogurt   * ¼ cup hazelnuts, chopped
* ¼ cup **Ayhan's Famous dried fruit of choice**, diced

Directions: Dice dried fruit and hazel nuts and sprinkle on top of frozen yogurt

Snack 1 Pear (82 cals)

Prep Time: 1 minute   **Total Time:** 1 minute

Ingredients
* 1 pear

Nutrition Facts	
Calories	217
Total Fat	9g
Saturated Fat	3g
Cholesterol	11mg
Sodium	63mg
Total Carbs	32g
Dietary Fiber	3g
Sugars	22g
Protein	5g

Day 11 Meal Plan and Recipes

Breakfast — Fruit Smoothie (248 cals)

Prep time: 5 minutes   **Total time:** 5 minutes

Ingredients
* 1 cup non-fat milk
* 3/4 cup frozen berries
* 2 cups ice
* 1/2 banana, sliced
* 1/2 cup orange Juice
* 1 packet sugar substitute (if desired)

Directions: Place ingredients in blender and mix until desired consistency.

Nutrition Facts

Calories	248
Total Fat	1g
Saturated Fat	0g
Cholesterol	5mg
Sodium	135mg
Total Carbs	51g
Dietary Fiber	4g
Sugars	44g
Protein	11g

Lunch — Lentil and Walnut Salad (476 cals)

Prep Time: 5 minutes   **Cook Time:** 5 minutes   **Total Time:** 10 minutes

Ingredients
* 1/2 cup red lentils, dried   * 1/4 c. walnuts, chopped   * 2 c. salad greens
* 4 tbsp **Ayhan's Lite Mediterranean Vinaigrette Dressing and Marinade**
* 1 scallion, diced   * 1/2 cup water

Directions: Rinse lentils under cold water. Combine lentils with 1/2 cup of water in a 2 quart microwave safe dish. Microwave for 5 minutes. Drain any excess water and let lentils cool. Toss salad greens, walnuts and scallions with 2 tbsps of dressing. Mix lentils with remaining 2 tbsp of dressing, place on top of greens, and serve.

Nutrition Facts

Calories	476
Total Fat	22g
Saturated Fat	3g
Cholesterol	0mg
Sodium	542mg
Total Carbs	51g
Dietary Fiber	20g
Sugars	6g
Protein	23g

Dinner — Grilled Chicken and Artichoke Pizza (578 cals)

Prep Time: 5 minutes   **Cook Time:** 10 minutes   **Total Time:** 15 minutes

Temperature Instructions: Preheat oven to 450 degrees

Ingredients
* 1 whole wheat pita   * 3 ounces grilled chicken   * 1/2 cup **artichoke hearts**
* 2 ounces part-skim mozzarella cheese, shredded   * 2 tbsp tomato sauce
* 4 slices ripe tomato   * 3 tbsp **Ayhan's Lemon & Herb Dressing**

Directions: Baste chicken with Lemon & Herb Dressing and grill or bake at 450 degrees for about 5 minutes or until golden brown. Set aside. Split open the pita bread and toast for about 2 minutes. Take the pita out of the oven and spread tomato sauce and tomato slices on the surface. Top it with the cheese, artichokes and chicken. Place it back in the oven for about 2 minutes, until the cheese has melted.

Nutrition Facts

Calories	578
Total Fat	30g
Saturated Fat	10g
Cholesterol	77mg
Sodium	2514mg
Total Carbs	41g
Dietary Fiber	9g
Sugars	5g
Protein	43g

Dinner — Side Salad (64 cals)

Prep Time: 2 minutes   **Total Time:** 2 minutes

Ingredients
* 1 cup salad greens   * 1 tbsp **Ayhan's Lemon & Herb Dressing**

Directions: Toss salad greens with dressing and enjoy.

Nutrition Facts

Calories	64
Total Fat	6g
Total Carbs	2g

Snack — Honey Yogurt (172 cals)

Prep Time: 2 minutes   **Total Time:** 2 minutes

Ingredients
* 1-6 ounce container nonfat Greek yogurt or nonfat/plain yogurt
* 1 tbsp honey

Directions: Drizzle honey on top of yogurt and enjoy.

Nutrition Facts

Calories	172
Total Fat	4g
Saturated Fat	1g
Cholesterol	7mg
Sodium	20mg
Total Carbs	21g
Dietary Fiber	2g
Sugars	19g
Protein	19g

Day 12 Meal Plan and Recipes

Breakfast Fruit and Nut Cottage Cheese (216 cals)
Prep time: 3 minutes   **Total time:** 3 minutes
Ingredients
* ¾ cup nonfat cottage cheese
* ¼ cup **Ayhan's Famous dried fruit** of choice, diced
* 6 **Ayhan's Famous roasted almonds**
Directions: Top cottage cheese with dried fruit and almonds.

Nutrition Facts	
Calories	216
Total Fat	4g
Saturated Fat	0g
Cholesterol	0mg
Sodium	635mg
Total Carbs	26g
Dietary Fiber	3g
Sugars	22g
Protein	23g

Lunch Baked Falafel Sandwich w/ Lite Yogurt Dressing (398 cals)
Prep Time: 10 minutes   **Cook Time:** 15 minutes   **Total Time:** 25 minutes
Temperature Instructions: Preheat oven to 450 degrees.
Ingredients
* 1/3 cup **boxed falafel mix** (to make 4 falafel balls   * 1 cup salad greens
* 1/2 cup cucumber & tomato, chopped   * cooking spray   * 1 clove garlic, crushed
* 1 whole wheat pita   * 1/2 cup nonfat, plain yogurt (pref. non fat Greek yogurt)
* 1/2 cup diced cucumber   * 2 tbsp water   * salt and pepper, to taste
Directions: Prepare 4 falafel balls according to the box directions (about 1/3 of dry mixture). Instead of frying them, make 1/2 inch thin patties and bake for 8 minutes on each side, until lightly brown. Cut the pita bread in 1/2 and stuff with falafel balls, salad greens and cucumber and tomato mixture (put 2 falafels into each 1/2). For the dressing, combine the yogurt, cucumber, water, garlic and salt and pepper to taste. Blend them together. Pour the mixture into each 1/2 of the sandwich and serve.

Nutrition Facts	
Calories	398
Total Fat	5g
Saturated Fat	0g
Cholesterol	2mg
Sodium	973mg
Total Carbs	65g
Dietary Fiber	9g
Sugars	13g
Protein	22g

Dinner Quick Chicken Kebab w/ Basmati Rice & Spinach (596 cals)
Prep Time: 5 minutes   **Cook Time:** 15 minutes   **Total Time:** 20 minutes
Temperature Instructions: Preheat oven to 450 degrees
Ingredients
* 4 ounces chicken breast, cubed   * 5 tbsp **Ayhan's Lemon & Herb Dressing**
* 4 small mushrooms   * 4 onions, cut into 1" squares   * 4 grape tomatoes
* 2/3 cup **basmati rice**, cooked (for quick cook time use couscous)
* 2 tsp margarine   * 2 cups fresh spinach (or 1 cup frozen)
Directions: Cut chicken breast into 1" cubes. Baste with Ayhan's Lemon & Herb Dressing and arrange chicken, mushrooms, onions, and plum tomato on skewer (use vegetables to fill skewer) Bake in oven for 5 minutes. For Basmati Rice: Prepare as directed on package without added fat and melt margarine into rice after cooked. For Steamed Spinach: Use 2 cups fresh spinach or one cup frozen. Place in covered pot, without any added water. Steam until spinach cooks down.

Nutrition Facts	
Calories	596
Total Fat	29g
Saturated Fat	4g
Cholesterol	66mg
Sodium	896mg
Total Carbs	52g
Dietary Fiber	6g
Sugars	12g
Protein	35g

Snack Orange Cream Smoothie (157 cals)
Prep Time: 5 minutes   **Total Time:** 5 minutes
Ingredients
* 1 cup nonfat milk   * 1 fresh orange   * 1 tsp vanilla extract
* 1 packet sugar substitute   * 2 cups ice
Directions: Place all ingredients in blender and blend to desired consistency.

Nutrition Facts	
Calories	157
Total Fat	1g
Total Carbs	27g

Snack 1 Apple (81 cals)
Prep Time: 1 minute   **Total Time:** 1 minute
Ingredients: 1 apple

Day 13 Meal Plan and Recipes

Breakfast — Yogurt Parfait (280 cals)

Prep time: 5 minutes   **Total time:** 5 minutes

Ingredients
* ½ cup bran cereal   * 2/3 cup plain, nonfat Greek yogurt
* 4 **Ayhan's Famous dried Turkish apricots**, cut into small pieces
* 6 almonds, chopped

Directions: In a tall glass, place a bottom layer of yogurt, a layer of apricots, and a layer of bran cereal, then repeat. Top parfait with chopped almonds.

Nutrition Facts

Calories	280
Total Fat	5g
Saturated Fat	0g
Cholesterol	7mg
Sodium	283mg
Total Carbs	57g
Dietary Fiber	15g
Sugars	28g
Protein	15g

Lunch — Tel-Aviv Salad with Grilled Chicken (415 cals)

Prep Time: 5 minutes **Cook Time:** 15 minutes **Total Time:** 20 minutes

Temperature Instructions: Preheat oven to 450 degrees.

Ingredients
* 2 red tomatoes   * 2 Kirby cucumbers   * 3 tbsp parsley, diced
* 2/3 cup **couscous**, cooked   * 3 ounces chicken breast, grilled
* 4 tbsp **Ayhan's Lite Mediterranean Vinaigrette Dressing and Marinade**

Directions: Bake or grill chicken for 5 minutes and set aside. Dice tomatoes and cucumbers and set aside. Prepare couscous according to package directions without added oil. Combine all ingredients and toss.

Nutrition Facts

Calories	415
Total Fat	17g
Saturated Fat	3g
Cholesterol	15mg
Sodium	997mg
Total Carbs	53g
Dietary Fiber	7g
Sugars	6g
Protein	14g

Dinner — Lamb Kebab Sandwich w/ Lite Yogurt Dressing (571 cals)

Prep Time: 10 minutes **Cook Time:** 15 minutes **Total Time:** 25 minutes

Temperature Instructions: Preheat oven to 450 degrees

Ingredients
* 3 oz lean lamb, cubed   * 1/2 c. ripe tomato, diced   * 1 cup salad greens
* 3 tbsp **Ayhan's Lemon & Herb Dressing and Marinade**
* 1 whole wheat pocket pita   * salt and pepper, to taste
* 1/2 cup non-fat, plain yogurt (pref. non fat Greek yogurt)
* 1/2 cup cucumber, diced   * 2 tbsp water   * 1 clove garlic, diced

Directions: Baste lamb cubes with Ayhan's Lemon & Herb Dressing and grill or bake 8 minutes each side. Stuff into pita with tomatoes and salad greens. Top with yogurt sauce. (Yogurt sauce: Mix yogurt, cucumber, garlic, and water. Add salt and pepper to taste.)

Nutrition Facts

Calories	571
Total Fat	31g
Saturated Fat	8g
Cholesterol	64mg
Sodium	863mg
Total Carbs	47g
Dietary Fiber	8g
Sugars	12g
Protein	32g

Snack — Cottage Cheese and Melon (79 cals)

Prep Time: 3 minutes   **Total Time:** 3 minutes

Ingredients
* 1 cup cubed melon   * ¼ cup nonfat cottage cheese

Directions: Serve cottage cheese topped with cubed melon

Nutrition Facts

Calories	79
Total Fat	0g
Total Carbs	13g

Snack — Nutty Apple Slices (176 cals)

Prep Time: 3 minutes   **Total Time:** 3 minutes

Ingredients
* 1 medium sized apple
* 1 tbsp all natural peanut butter or almond butter

Directions: Slice apple and spread nut butter on slices.

Nutrition Facts

Calories	176
Total Fat	9g
Saturated Fat	2g
Cholesterol	0mg
Sodium	3mg
Total Carbs	24g
Dietary Fiber	5g
Sugars	18g
Protein	4g

Day 14 Meal Plan and Recipes

Breakfast Mediterranean Spinach and Olive Omelette (392 cals)

Prep time: 5 minutes   **Cook Time:** 5 minutes   **Total time:** 5 minutes

Ingredients
* 4 egg whites   * 1/2 cup frozen spinach
* 1 tsp olive oil   * 8 **black olives**, sliced
* 1/2 whole wheat pita toasted, or 1 mini whole wheat pita toasted
* 1 cup nonfat milk   * 1 cup melon cubed

Directions: Mix egg whites, spinach, and olives in a bowl. Heat 1 tsp olive oil in skillet and pour egg mixture in. Cook until eggs set and then flip. Serve the omelette with 1/2 whole wheat pita, milk, and melon cubes.

Nutrition Facts

Calories	392
Total Fat	10g
Saturated Fat	2g
Cholesterol	5mg
Sodium	786mg
Total Carbs	50g
Dietary Fiber	7g
Sugars	26g
Protein	31g

Lunch Babaganoush Pizza (479 cals)

Prep Time: 10 minutes   **Cook Time:** 30 minutes   **Total Time:** 40 minutes

Temperature Instructions: Preheat oven to 450 degrees.

Ingredients
* 1 whole wheat pita   * 2 ounces fat free feta cheese   * 1/4 cup lemon juice
* 1 medium eggplant   * 1/4 cup tahini   * 1-2 garlic cloves, crushed
* 1/3 cup babaganoush (puree of eggplant; can be found in grocery store)
* 1 tsp olive oil   * dash of salt (optional)   * dash of parsley (optional)

Directions: To make homemade Babaganoush: Preheat oven to 450 degrees. Pierce the eggplant with a fork a few times and bake for about 30 minutes or until tender and somewhat deflated. Mash, chop, or puree the eggplant depending on how you want it. Then add the lemon juice, tahini, garlic olive oil, salt and parsley. Mix well and serve at room temperature. To prepare the pizza: Open whole wheat pita and toast in a conventional or toaster oven at 450 degrees for about 1-2 minutes, until golden brown and crispy. Spread babaganoush over each side of pizza and sprinkle cheese on top. Place back in the oven for about 2 more minutes to warm.

Nutrition Facts

Calories	479
Total Fat	21g
Saturated Fat	8g
Cholesterol	50mg
Sodium	1183mg
Total Carbs	42g
Dietary Fiber	41g
Sugars	4g
Protein	19g

Dinner Salmon Delite (414 cals)

Prep Time: 10 minutes   **Total Time:** 10 minutes

Ingredients
* 1 cup tomatoes, diced   * 1 cup cucumber, diced
* 1/2 cup green pepper, diced   * 1 tbsp parsley, chopped
* 1/4 cup low fat feta cheese, crumbled   * 4 oz canned sockeye salmon
* 3 tbsp **Ayhan's Lite Mediterranean Vinaigrette**

Directions: Combine all ingredients except salmon and toss with dressing. Top mixture with salmon, chill, and serve.

Nutrition Facts

Calories	414
Total Fat	23g
Saturated Fat	7g
Cholesterol	60mg
Sodium	1496mg
Total Carbs	20g
Dietary Fiber	5g
Sugars	7g
Protein	33g

Dinner Side Salad (64 cals)

Prep Time: 2 minutes   **Total Time:** 2 minutes

Ingredients
* 1 cup salad greens
* 1 tbsp **Ayhan's Lemon & Herb Dressing** or **Mediterranean Vinaigrette**

Directions: Toss salad greens with dressing and enjoy.

Nutrition Facts

Calories	64
Total Fat	0g
Total Carbs	13g

Snack 1 Orange (65 cals)

Prep Time: 1 minute   **Total Time:** 1 minute

Ingredients
* 1 orange

Nutrition Facts

Calories	65
Total Fat	0g
Total Carbs	16g

Ayhan's
Mediterranean Menu
Plans®

Week 3

Day 15 Meal Plan and Recipes

Breakfast Nut Butter Banana Sandwich (292 cals)
Prep time: 5 minutes   **Total time:** 5 minutes
Ingredients
* 1/2 whole wheat English muffin
* 1 tbsp all natural nut butter (peanut, almond, or cashew)
* 1 small banana, sliced
* 1 tbsp honey

Directions: Toast English muffin. Top with nut butter, banana and drizzle with honey.

Nutrition Facts	
Calories	292
Total Fat	9g
Saturated Fat	2g
Cholesterol	0mg
Sodium	286mg
Total Carbs	51g
Dietary Fiber	5g
Sugars	33g
Protein	8g

Breakfast Fat-free or Soy Milk (86 cals)
Prep time: 1 minute   **Total time:** 1 minute
Ingredients
* 1 cup fat-free or soy milk

Nutrition Facts	
Calories	86
Total Fat	0g
Total Carbs	12g

Lunch High Fiber Burger and Salad (490 cals)
Prep Time: 5 minutes   **Cook Time:** 5 minutes   **Total Time:** 10 minutes
Ingredients
* 1/4 medium avocado, sliced   * 1 patty black bean or veggie burger (premade/frozen)
* 1/2 whole wheat pita   * 1/4 cup mandarin oranges, canned and drained
* 6 **Ayhan's Famous almonds**   * 2 cups salad greens, chopped
* 2 tbsp **Ayhan's Balsamic Vinaigrette Dressing**

Directions: Toss oranges, almonds and salad greens with Ayhan's Balsamic Vinaigrette and set aside. Heat veggie burger according to package directions. Top burger with avocado slices and stuff into 1/2 pita bread. Serve veggie burger with salad.

Nutrition Facts	
Calories	490
Total Fat	27g
Saturated Fat	4g
Cholesterol	2mg
Sodium	619mg
Total Carbs	45g
Dietary Fiber	16g
Sugars	17g
Protein	25g

Dinner Grilled Salmon and Greens (495 cals)
Prep Time: 9 minutes   **Cook Time:** 6 minutes   **Total Time:** 15 minutes
Ingredients
* 3 ounces salmon filet   * 3 cups fresh baby spinach
* 1 cup green beans, cooked and chilled   * 1/2 lemon, juice of
* salt and pepper, to taste   * 1 cup plum tomatoes, diced
* 4 tbsp **Ayhan's Lite Mediterranean Vinaigrette Dressing and Marinade**

Directions: Sprinkle salmon with lemon juice, salt and pepper. Grill or bake 3 minutes each side. Steam green beans for about 2 minutes. Toss spinach, green beans, and tomatoes with Ayhan's Lite Vinaigrette Dressing. Serve salmon on bed of greens.

Nutrition Facts	
Calories	495
Total Fat	22g
Saturated Fat	4g
Cholesterol	66mg
Sodium	2247mg
Total Carbs	38g
Dietary Fiber	18g
Sugars	8g
Protein	38g

Snack Smoothie (241 cals)
Prep Time: 5 minutes   **Total Time:** 5 minutes
Ingredients
* 1 cup fat-free or soy milk   * 1 tbsp honey
* 1 1/4 cup strawberries   * 2 cups ice
* 1 packet sugar substitute (if desired)

Directions: Blend above ingredients in blender for approximately 1 minute, or until desired consistency.

Nutrition Facts	
Calories	241
Total Fat	2g
Saturated Fat	0g
Cholesterol	5mg
Sodium	128mg
Total Carbs	54g
Dietary Fiber	4g
Sugars	46g
Protein	10g

Day 16 Meal Plan and Recipes

Breakfast — Granola Yogurt (335 cals)

Prep time: 2 minutes   **Total time:** 2 minutes

Ingredients
* 2oz **Ayhan's Famous Granola** (any variety) or any other granola
* 6 oz fat free Greek style yogurt (Total Fage 0%) or plain, non fat yogurt

Directions: Sprinkle granola and cranberries on top of yogurt and enjoy.

Nutrition Facts

Calories	335
Total Fat	12g
Saturated Fat	2g
Cholesterol	3mg
Sodium	131mg
Total Carbs	43g
Dietary Fiber	4g
Sugars	21g
Protein	18g

Lunch — Radicchio, Artichoke, Olive and Walnut Salad with Tuna Fish (416 cals)

Prep Time: 10 minutes   **Total Time:** 10 minutes

Ingredients
* 1/2 cup canned **artichoke hearts**, drained and sliced
* 4 **Ayhan's Famous walnut halves**, chopped
* 4 tbsp **Ayhan's Lite Mediterranean Vinaigrette Dressing and Marinade**
* 2 cups radicchio, chopped (a variety of lettuce)   * 8 **black olives**, sliced
* 1/2 cup plain croutons   * 3 oz tuna fish, canned in water and drained

Directions: Toss all ingredients with Ayhan's Lite Vinaigrette Dressing and enjoy.

Nutrition Facts

Calories	416
Total Fat	21g
Saturated Fat	3g
Cholesterol	26mg
Sodium	1431mg
Total Carbs	29g
Dietary Fiber	7g
Sugars	2g
Protein	29g

Dinner — Breaded Shrimp with Marinated Diced Tomato (323 cals)

Prep Time: 5 minutes   **Cook Time:** 10 minutes   **Total Time:** 15 minutes

Temperature Instructions: Preheat oven to 450 degrees

Ingredients
* 5 jumbo shrimp, peeled and de-veined   * 4 tbsp **Ayhan's Lite Mediterranean Vinaigrette**
* 1/4 cup seasoned breadcrumbs   * 2 cup salad greens, chopped
* 1 cup ripe tomato, diced   * 2 tbsp **Ayhan's Famous Balsamic Dressing**

Directions: Dip shrimp in 4 Tbsp. lite dressing and dredge in breadcrumbs. Skewer and grill or bake for 10 minutes. Place kebab over salad greens, set aside. Mix tomato with balsamic dressing. Place marinated tomatoes over the shrimp and serve.

Nutrition Facts

Calories	323
Total Fat	13g
Saturated Fat	2g
Cholesterol	46mg
Sodium	1841mg
Total Carbs	30g
Dietary Fiber	11g
Sugars	9g
Protein	17g

Snack — Banana Smoothie (142 cals)

Prep Time: 3 minutes   **Total Time:** 3 minutes

Ingredients
* 8 oz fat-free milk   * ½ banana/1 small banana   * 2 c. ice
* 2 packets sugar substitute

Directions: Blend above ingredients in blender for approximately 1 minute.

Nutrition Facts

Calories	142
Total Fat	1g
Total Carbs	26g

Snack — Grapes (70 cals)

Prep Time: 1 minute   **Total Time:** 1 minute

Ingredients: 17 grapes

Directions: Serve grapes and enjoy! Option: place grapes in a Tupperware container and freeze the night before. Enjoy a frozen treat.

Nutrition Facts

Calories	70
Total Fat	1g
Total Carbs	18g

Snack — Cottage Cheese and Wheat Germ (183 cals)

Prep Time: 2 minutes   **Total Time:** 2 minutes

Ingredients
* ½ cup low fat cottage cheese   * 3 tbsp wheat germ

Directions: Sprinkle wheat germ over cottage cheese and serve.

Nutrition Facts

Calories	183
Total Fat	4g
Total Carbs	15g

Day 17 Meal Plan and Recipes

Breakfast Ricotta and Berry Pita (188 cals)
Prep time: 3 minutes   **Total time:** 3 minutes
Ingredients
  * 1/4 cup part skim ricotta cheese
  * 1/2 whole wheat pita
  * 3/4 cup mixed berries
Directions: Mix ricotta cheese and berries. Heat pita bread. Cut open and stuff with mixture.

Nutrition Facts

Calories	188
Total Fat	6g
Saturated Fat	3g
Cholesterol	19mg
Sodium	236mg
Total Carbs	27g
Dietary Fiber	4g
Sugars	9g
Protein	11g

Lunch Lentil Soup and Cucumber Salad with Yogurt Dressing (361 cals)
Prep Time: 10 minutes   **Total Time:** 10 minutes
Ingredients
  * 2 cups canned lentil soup   * 3 oz fat free, plain yogurt
  * 1 large cucumber, sliced   * 1 clove garlic, crushed
  * 2 tsp white wine vinegar   * salt and pepper, to taste
Directions: Mix 3 ounces fat-free plain yogurt with 1 clove crushed garlic and 2 tsp white wine vinegar. Add salt and pepper to taste. Pour mixture over cucumber slices and gently mix together, set aside. Heat soup according to directions and serve salad alongside soup.

Nutrition Facts

Calories	361
Total Fat	5g
Saturated Fat	1g
Cholesterol	8mg
Sodium	958mg
Total Carbs	55g
Dietary Fiber	14g
Sugars	8g
Protein	22g

Lunch Croutons (122 cals)
Prep Time: 1 minute   **Total Time:** 1 minute
Ingredients: 1 cup plain croutons
Directions: Sprinkle over soup and enjoy.

Nutrition Facts

Calories	122
Total Fat	2g
Total Carbs	55g

Dinner Low Calorie Sicilian Antipasto (371 cals)
Prep Time: 10 minutes   **Total Time:** 10 minutes
Ingredients
  * 2 cups salad greens, sliced   * 2 cups plum tomatoes, diced
  * 1/2 cup canned **artichoke hearts**, sliced   * 1 tbsp capers
  * 3 ounces tuna, packed in water   * 3 small radishes, sliced
  * 1/2 cup red or green peppers, diced
  * 3 tbsp **Ayhan's Lite Mediterranean Dressing**
Directions: Toss all ingredients with Ayhan's Lite Dressing. Chill and serve.

Nutrition Facts

Calories	371
Total Fat	23g
Saturated Fat	3g
Cholesterol	0mg
Sodium	1420mg
Total Carbs	18g
Dietary Fiber	5g
Sugars	6g
Protein	27g

Dinner Café Con Leche (100 cals)
Prep Time: 5 minutes   **Total Time:** 5 minutes
Ingredients
  * 1 cup fat-free milk, steamed   * 1/2 cup decaf espresso
  * 1 packet artificial sweetener
Directions: Combine ingredients and enjoy.

Nutrition Facts

Calories	100
Total Fat	1g
Total Carbs	14g

Snack Nutty Apple Slices (303 cals)
Prep Time: 2 minutes   **Total Time:** 2 minutes
Ingredients
  * 1 apple, sliced   * 1½ tbsp all natural peanut butter
  * ½ cup fat-free or soy milk, to drink
Directions: Spread peanut butter over apple slices and serve with milk.

Nutrition Facts

Calories	303
Total Fat	14g
Total Carbs	34g

Snack 3 Dates (68 cals)
Prep Time: 1 minute   **Total Time:** 1 minute
Ingredients: 3 dates

Nutrition Facts

Calories	68
Total Fat	0g
Total Carbs	18g

Day 18 Meal Plan and Recipes

Breakfast — Orange-Apricot Pancakes (336 cals)

Prep time: 10 minutes   **Cook Time:** 5 minutes   **Total time:** 15 minutes

Ingredients
* 2 pancakes made from whole wheat pancake mix   * 1 tbsp **Hai orange jam**
* 1 cup fat free milk for pancake mix (amount may vary depending on pancake mix)
* 4 **Ayhan's Famous dried apricots**, diced   * 1 tbsp canola oil for pancake mix
* 2 egg whites   * cooking spray

Directions: Prepare 2 pancakes, each the size of a compact disc, as per box directions using egg whites instead of whole eggs, fat free mil, and canola oil (some mixes may omit some of these ingredients). Use cooking spray to grease the pan. Cook each side until golden brown. Spread orange jam on hot pancakes and top with diced apricots..

Nutrition Facts

Calories	336
Total Fat	8g
Saturated Fat	2g
Cholesterol	69mg
Sodium	761mg
Total Carbs	51g
Dietary Fiber	6g
Sugars	22g
Protein	18g

Lunch — Grilled Chicken Salad (383 cals)

Prep Time: 10 minutes   **Cook Time:** 5 minutes   **Total Time:** 15 minutes
Temperature Instructions: Preheat oven to 450 degrees

Ingredients
* 2 cups mixed greens, chopped   * 1 cup ripe tomato, diced
* 1/4 cup red kidney beans, canned (drained and rinsed)
* 8 **Maroli green olives** with lemon
* 3 ounces grilled chicken breast, cut into strips
* 3 tbsp **Ayhan's Lite Mediterranean Dressing**

Directions: Grill chicken on a grill pan or in the oven at 450 degrees for approx. 5 minutes and set aside to cool. Toss all ingredients with dressing. Chill and serve.

Nutrition Facts

Calories	383
Total Fat	14g
Saturated Fat	2g
Cholesterol	47mg
Sodium	2827mg
Total Carbs	33g
Dietary Fiber	13g
Sugars	8g
Protein	30g

Dinner — Healthy Mediterranean Spinach Pizza (486 cals)

Prep Time: 5 minutes   **Cook Time:** 10 minutes   **Total Time:** 15 minutes
Temperature Instructions: Preheat oven to 450 degrees

Ingredients
* 1 whole wheat pita   * 2 cups fresh baby leaf spinach (or 1 cup frozen, thawed)
* 2 tsp olive oil   * 1 clove garlic, chopped
* 2 ounces low-fat mozzarella cheese   * 1 ounce low-fat ricotta cheese

Directions: Open pita bread and drizzle 1 tsp olive oil on each side. Place in oven and toast for 1-2 minutes. Place ricotta cheese on each side, then raw baby spinach leaves, then mozzarella cheese. Bake in oven until cheese is melted.

Nutrition Facts

Calories	486
Total Fat	23g
Saturated Fat	9g
Cholesterol	39mg
Sodium	781mg
Total Carbs	45g
Dietary Fiber	9g
Sugars	2g
Protein	29g

Snack — Almond Yogurt & Banana (224 cals)

Prep Time: 3 minutes   **Total Time:** 3 minutes

Ingredients
* 1 cup fat-free Greek yogurt
* ½ large/1 small banana, sliced
* 6 **Ayhan's Famous Almonds**

Directions: Top yogurt with bananas and almonds and enjoy.

Nutrition Facts

Calories	224
Total Fat	4g
Saturated Fat	0g
Cholesterol	10mg
Sodium	151mg
Total Carbs	36g
Dietary Fiber	2g
Sugars	28g
Protein	13g

Snack — 1 Cup of Melon (44 cals)

Prep Time: 2 minute   **Total Time:** 2 minute

Ingredients
* 1 cup melon, cubed

Nutrition Facts

Calories	44
Total Fat	0g
Total Carbs	11g

Ayhan's Grilled Chicken Salad

Day 19 Meal Plan and Recipes

Breakfast — Cheesy Egg White Pita (334 cals)

Prep time: 5 minutes **Cook Time:** 5 minutes **Total time:** 10 minutes

Ingredients
* 2 egg whites   * 1 tsp olive oil   * 1 ounce low-fat feta cheese
* 1/2 whole wheat pita   * 1 tomato slice   * 1/2 cup leafy greens, chopped
* 1/2 cup orange juice, to drink

Directions: Heat olive oil in pan, add egg whites, and cook until white, approx. 3 minutes. Sprinkle cheese over eggs. Cut open pita pocket. Stuff with greens, eggs and tomatoes. Serve with 1/2 cup orange juice.

Nutrition Facts

Calories	334
Total Fat	13g
Saturated Fat	6g
Cholesterol	34mg
Sodium	827mg
Total Carbs	22g
Dietary Fiber	5g
Sugars	6g
Protein	31g

Lunch — Baked Stuffed Tomatoes (381 cals)

Prep Time: 5 minutes **Cook Time:** 30 minutes **Total Time:** 35 minutes

Temperature Instructions: Preheat oven to 450 degrees

Ingredients
* 2/3 cup **Near East Rice Pilaf**, cooked (for quick cook time use couscous)
* 1/4 cup Spanish onion, chopped   * 1 garlic clove, crushed
* 1 tbsp fresh parsley, chopped   * 2 tbsp **Ayhan's Famous golden raisins**
* 3 tbsp chopped almonds   * 1 tbsp parmesan   * 2 large tomatoes
* salt and pepper to taste

Directions: Prepare rice pilaf according to package directions, without added oil or butter. Mix together the rice pilaf, onion, garlic, parsley, raisins, almonds, parmesan cheese, and salt and pepper to taste and set aside. Cut tomatoes across the top and scoop out pulp. Dice the pulp and add to the above mixture. Stuff the tomatoes with rice mixture. Bake at 450 degrees for 10 minutes, or until top is golden brown.

Nutrition Facts

Calories	381
Total Fat	11g
Saturated Fat	2g
Cholesterol	7mg
Sodium	766mg
Total Carbs	61g
Dietary Fiber	6g
Sugars	24g
Protein	15g

Lunch — Side Salad (64 cals)

Prep Time: 2 minutes   **Total Time:** 2 minutes

Ingredients
* 1 c. salad greens
* 1 tbsp **Ayhan's Lemon & Herb Dressing** or **Mediterranean Vinaigrette**

Directions: Toss salad greens with dressing and enjoy.

Nutrition Facts

Calories	64
Total Fat	6g
Saturated Fat	1g
Cholesterol	0g
Sodium	134mg
Total Carbs	2g
Dietary Fiber	1g
Sugars	0g
Protein	1g

Dinner — Grilled Sea Bass or Striped Bass w/ Couscous and Asparagus (419 cals)

Prep Time: 15 minutes **Cook Time:** 15 minutes **Total Time:** 30 minutes

Ingredients
* 4 ounces sea bass or striped bass   * 2 tsp olive oil   * juice of 1/2 lemon
* 2/3 cup **Near East Roasted Toasted Pine Nut Couscous**, cooked
* 4 asparagus stalks
* 2 tbsp **Ayhan's Lite Mediterranean Vinaigrette Dressing and Marinade**

Directions: Heat olive oil in saucepan. Sautee fish until tender. Sprinkle with lemon juice. Cook couscous according to package directions, without any added oil. Steam asparagus for about 3-4 minutes. Toss asparagus with Ayhan's Lite Vinaigrette. Serve fish over couscous with asparagus on the side.

Nutrition Facts

Calories	419
Total Fat	18g
Saturated Fat	3g
Cholesterol	60mg
Sodium	371mg
Total Carbs	30g
Dietary Fiber	3g
Sugars	3g
Protein	32g

Snack — Vanilla Yogurt & Cantaloupe (221 cals)

Prep Time: 3 minutes   **Total Time:** 3 minutes

Ingredients
* 1 cup cantaloupe cubes   * 6 ounces low fat vanilla yogurt

Directions: Top yogurt with cantaloupe and enjoy.

Nutrition Facts

Calories	221
Total Fat	3g
Total Carbs	43g

Day 20 Meal Plan and Recipes

Breakfast — Cranberry and Almond Yogurt Parfait (294 cals)

Prep time: 3 minutes   **Total time:** 3 minutes

Ingredients
* 6oz container of fat free Greek style yogurt or fat free, plain yogurt
* 1 oz **Ayhan's Famous dried cranberries**   * 1 tbsp honey
* 6 **Ayhan's Famous roasted almonds**

Directions: Using a tall glass, place 1/2 of the yogurt from your container into the bottom, drizzle the honey over the yogurt, place the almonds over the honey, scoop the rest of the yogurt over the almonds, and top with the cranberries. This will create a layered parfait.

Nutrition Facts

Calories	294
Total Fat	6g
Saturated Fat	2g
Cholesterol	15mg
Sodium	243mg
Total Carbs	34g
Dietary Fiber	1g
Sugars	24g
Protein	11g

Lunch — Anatolian Salad (508 cals)

Prep Time: 10 minutes   **Total Time:** 10 minutes

Ingredients
* 1 cup plum tomato, diced   * 3 cups salad greens, shredded
* 1 cup Kirby cucumbers, diced   * 8 **kalamata olives**
* 1/2 cup fresh green beans, chopped   * 1/4 tsp fresh basil, chopped
* 3 pieces **anchovy fillets**, chopped (or 3 oz tuna canned in water, drained)
* 1/2 toasted whole wheat pita   * salt and pepper
* 4 tbsp **Ayhan's Mediterranean Vinaigrette Dressing and Marinade**

Directions: Toss ingredients with Ayhan's Mediterranean Vinaigrette Dressing. Add salt and pepper to taste. Serve with hot pita.

Nutrition Facts

Calories	508
Total Fat	23g
Saturated Fat	3g
Cholesterol	51mg
Sodium	2781mg
Total Carbs	36g
Dietary Fiber	15g
Sugars	8g
Protein	32g

Dinner — Pan-fried Falafel and Spinach Sandwich (434 cals)

Prep Time: 3 minutes **Cook Time:** 10 minutes **Total Time:** 13 mins

Ingredients
* 1/3 cup mix **falafel mix**   * 2 tsp olive oil   * 1 cup fresh baby leaf spinach
* 1 whole wheat pita   * cooking spray

Directions: Prepare 4 falafel balls (1/3 cup mix) according to box instructions. Form into balls. Heat olive oil in a non-stick skillet and sauté falafel balls until golden brown. Use extra cooking spray as needed to avoid sticking. Set aside. Cut pita bread in half and stuff each side with 2 falafel balls and spinach.

Nutrition Facts

Calories	434
Total Fat	9g
Saturated Fat	1g
Cholesterol	0mg
Sodium	1382mg
Total Carbs	63g
Dietary Fiber	11g
Sugars	1g
Protein	19g

Dinner — Yogurt Dressing (46 cals)

Prep Time: 5 minutes   **Total Time:** 5 minutes

Ingredients
* 1/2 c fat-free plain yogurt   * 1 clove garlic   * 2 tsp white wine vinegar
* 1/2 cup diced cucumber   * 1 tsp water   * salt and pepper to taste

Directions: Blend together yogurt, garlic, vinegar, cucumber and water. Blend very well. Add salt and pepper to taste. Drizzle mixture into each half of the falafel sandwich and serve.

Nutrition Facts

Calories	48
Total Fat	0g
Total Carbs	8g

Snack — Cottage Cheese & Pineapple (198 cals)

Prep Time: 3 minutes   **Total Time:** 3 minutes

Ingredients
* 1 cup fat-free cottage cheese   * ½ cup fresh or canned pineapple, diced

Directions: Top cottage cheese with pineapple and enjoy.

Nutrition Facts

Calories	198
Total Fat	0g
Total Carbs	22g

Snack — 1 Orange (64 cals)

Prep Time: 1 minute   **Total Time:** 1 minute

Ingredients: 1 orange

Directions: Eat and enjoy.

Nutrition Facts

Calories	64
Total Fat	0g
Total Carbs	16g

Day 21 Meal Plan and Recipes

Breakfast — Banana, Nut Cereal (330 cals)

Prep time: 3 minutes   **Total time:** 3 minutes

Ingredients
* 3/4 cup whole grain cereal
* 1/2 large or 1 small banana, sliced
* 1 cup fat-free milk or soy milk
* 6 **Ayhan's Famous Roasted Almonds**

Directions: Top cereal with sliced banana and almonds. Pour milk on top and serve.

Nutrition Facts

Calories	330
Total Fat	5g
Saturated Fat	1g
Cholesterol	5mg
Sodium	277mg
Total Carbs	62g
Dietary Fiber	9g
Sugars	31g
Protein	16g

Lunch — Spinach and Mushroom Frittata (411 cals)

Prep Time: 10 minutes **Cook Time:** 10 minutes **Total Time:** 10 minutes

Ingredients
* 4 egg whites
* 1 cup fresh, baby spinach leaves
* 1/2 cup mushrooms
* 2 tsp olive oil
* 2 tsp parmesan cheese
* salt and pepper, to taste

Directions: Heat olive oil in a saucepan. Sautee spinach and mushrooms until tender. Sprinkle with parmesan cheese, salt and pepper to taste. Pour egg whites over spinach, do not stir, cover and cook for about 3-4 minutes.

Nutrition Facts

Calories	411
Total Fat	31g
Saturated Fat	6g
Cholesterol	8mg
Sodium	887mg
Total Carbs	9g
Dietary Fiber	4g
Sugars	2g
Protein	25g

Lunch — Whole Wheat Bread and Fig Jam (106 cals)

Prep Time: 2 minutes   **Total Time:** 2 minutes

Ingredients
* 1 slice whole wheat bread
* 1 tbsp **Fig Jam**

Directions: Toast whole wheat bread and spread fig jam on top.

Nutrition Facts

Calories	106
Total Fat	3g
Total Carbs	23g

Dinner — Seafood Risotto (394 cals)

Prep Time: 10 minutes **Cook Time:** 15 minutes **Total Time:** 25 minutes

Ingredients
* 3 ounces shrimp, peeled and cut in pieces
* 3 ounces canned clams, drained
* 1/2 cup ripe tomatoes, diced
* 3 tsp olive oil
* 2 cloves garlic, crushed
* 2/3 cup **risotto**, cooked without added fat, according to package instructions

Directions: Heat olive oil and crushed garlic in saucepan for about 1-2 minutes. Sauté shrimp, clams, and tomatoes for about 5 minutes. Prepare risotto according to box directions, without any added fat. Measure out 2/3 cup of risotto, top with seafood, and serve.

Nutrition Facts

Calories	394
Total Fat	16g
Saturated Fat	2g
Cholesterol	158mg
Sodium	180mg
Total Carbs	29g
Dietary Fiber	1g
Sugars	0g
Protein	31g

Dinner — Side Salad (64 cals)

Prep Time: 5 minutes   **Total Time:** 5 minutes

Ingredients
* 1 cup salad greens
* 1 tbsp **Ayhan's Lemon & Herb Dressing** or **Mediterranean Vinaigrette**

Directions: Toss salad greens with dressing and enjoy.

Nutrition Facts

Calories	64
Total Fat	6g
Total Carbs	2g

Snack — Cranberry Health Mix (145 cals)

Prep Time: 1 minute   **Total Time:** 1 minute

Ingredients
* 1 cup **Ayhan's Famous Cranberry Health Mix**

Directions: Eat and enjoy.

Nutrition Facts

Calories	145
Total Fat	7g
Saturated Fat	1g
Cholesterol	0mg
Sodium	45mg
Total Carbs	16g
Dietary Fiber	2g
Sugars	13g
Protein	3g

Ayhan's
Mediterranean Menu Plans®

Week 4

Day 22 Meal Plan and Recipes

Breakfast Almond Honey Oatmeal (362 cals)
Prep time: 10 minutes   **Total time:** 10 minutes
Ingredients
  * 1/2 cup cooked oatmeal   * 1 tbsp honey
  * 2 tbsp raisins   '   * 6 **Ayhan's Famous roasted almonds**, chopped
Directions: Use 1 packet of instant, plain oatmeal and microwave according to package directions. Top with honey, raisins, and almonds. Or, use 1 packet of flavored and skip the honey and raisins, add the almonds.

Nutrition Facts	
Calories	362
Total Fat	6g
Saturated Fat	1g
Cholesterol	2mg
Sodium	66mg
Total Carbs	66g
Dietary Fiber	6g
Sugars	37g
Protein	12g

Lunch Fruit and Cheese Plate (308 cals)
Prep Time: 5 minutes   **Total Time:** 5 minutes
Ingredients
  * 1/2 cup low-fat (fat free or 1%) cottage cheese   * 1/2 apple, sliced
  * 9 grapes   * 1/2 cup melon, cubed
  * 2 ounces low-fat cheddar cheese   * 3 rye crisps
Directions: Slice apples, melon, and cheese. Top cottage cheese with apples, grapes, melon, and cheddar cheese. Serve with crackers and enjoy.

Nutrition Facts	
Calories	308
Total Fat	6g
Saturated Fat	3g
Cholesterol	14mg
Sodium	637mg
Total Carbs	43g
Dietary Fiber	6g
Sugars	23g
Protein	24g

Dinner Chicken Kebab Salad (404 cals)
Prep Time: 10 minutes **Cook Time:** 10 minutes **Total Time:** 20 minutes
Ingredients
  * 3 ounces chicken, ½ oz cubes   * 3 large mushrooms
  * 4 pieces onion, ¼ inch squares   * 3 cups salad greens, sliced
  * 2 tbsp **Ayhan's Lemon & Herb Dressing and Marinade**   * 8 **black olives**
  * 2 cups plum tomatoes, diced   * ½ cup Kirby cucumbers, diced
  * 3 tbsp **Ayhan's Lite Mediterranean Vinaigrette Dressing and Marinade**
Directions: Baste chicken, mushroom, and onions in Lemon Dressing and skewer chicken, mushroom, and onions. Grill or bake 5 minutes each side. Mix remaining ingredients with Ayhan's Lite Dressing and serve chicken kebab over salad.

Nutrition Facts	
Calories	404
Total Fat	27g
Saturated Fat	2g
Cholesterol	0mg
Sodium	918mg
Total Carbs	32g
Dietary Fiber	7g
Sugars	10g
Protein	12g

Dinner Café Con Leche (100 cals)
Prep Time: 5 minutes   **Total Time:** 5 minutes
Ingredients
  * 1 cup fat-free milk, steamed   * ½ cup decaf espresso
  * 1 packet artificial sweetener,
Directions: Combine ingredients and enjoy.

Nutrition Facts	
Calories	100
Total Fat	0g
Total Carbs	2g

Snack Hummus & Baby Carrots (304 cals)
Prep Time: 3 minutes   **Total Time:** 3 minutes
Ingredients
  * 1/3 cup hummus
  * 1 cup baby carrots
' * 1/2 cup Fat free or soy milk, to drink
Directions: Dip baby carrots into hummus and enjoy.

Nutrition Facts	
Calories	304
Total Fat	10g
Saturated Fat	2g
Cholesterol	5mg
Sodium	513mg
Total Carbs	41g
Dietary Fiber	9g
Sugars	22g
Protein	16g

Day 23 Meal Plan and Recipes

Breakfast Ham and Melon (258 cals)
Prep time: 5 minutes   **Total time:** 5 minutes
Ingredients
  * 3 thin slices lean ham   * 1 cup cantaloupe cubes
  * 1 cup fat-free milk or soy milk, to drink
Directions: Cut ham slices into quarters. Wrap ham around melon cubes. Secure with toothpicks and enjoy. Serve with 1 cup milk.

Nutrition Facts
Calories	258
Total Fat	6g
Total Carbs	26g

Lunch Baked Garlic Pita Chips (180 cals)
Prep Time: 3 minutes   **Cook Time:** 3 minutes   **Total Time:** 6 mins
Ingredients
  * 1 whole wheat pita   * 1 tsp olive oil   * 1 tsp garlic powder
  * 1/8 tsp salt   * 1/8 tsp pepper
Directions: Cut pita into 8 wedges. Brush pita with olive oil and top with garlic powder, salt and pepper. Place on cookie tray and cut into wedges. Bake at 450 degrees for 3 min., or until crisp.

Nutrition Facts
Calories	180
Total Fat	6g
Saturated Fat	1g
Cholesterol	0mg
Sodium	602mg
Total Carbs	30g
Dietary Fiber	5g
Sugars	2g
Protein	7g

Lunch Mediterranean Chicken Salad (420 cals)
Prep Time: 5 minutes **Cook Time:** 10 minutes   **Total Time:** 15 mins
Ingredients
  * 8 **small olives**   * 5 mushrooms, sliced   * 1/2 small red onion sliced
  * 3 c. lettuce, chopped   * 1 c. diced tomato   * 1/2 c. diced cucumber
  * 4 tbsp **Ayhan's Balsamic Vinaigrette**   * 4 oz grilled chicken breast
  * 1 oz feta cheese
Directions: Grill or bake chicken for 5 minutes on each side. Dice chicken and toss everything with Ayhan's Balsamic Vinaigrette and serve.

Dinner Quick Veggie Kebab (125 cals)
Prep Time: 5 minutes   **Cook Time:** 5 minutes **Total Time:** 10 mins
Ingredients
  * 4 pieces red or green bell peppers, cut into 1x1 inch squares
  * 4 pieces onions, cut 1"x1"   * 1 portabella mushroom, sliced
  * 4 grape tomatoes   * 2 tbsp **Ayhan's Lemon & Herb Dr**
Directions: Toss all vegetables with Ayhan's Lemon & Herb Dressing. Put on skewer, alternating peppers, onions, zucchini, mushrooms, tomatoes. Grill or bake for 5 minutes.

Nutrition Facts
Calories	125
Total Fat	12g
Saturated Fat	2g
Cholesterol	0mg
Sodium	262mg
Total Carbs	4g
Dietary Fiber	2g
Sugars	1g
Protein	14g

Dinner Lentil Soup (Each serving = 250 cals)
Prep Time: 5 minutes   **Cook Time:** 35 minutes   **Total Time:** 40 mins
Ingredients
  * 1 1/2 cup **red lentils**   * 8 cups chicken/vegetable broth
  * 1/4 cup chopped onions   * 2 tbsp olive oil   * 1 peeled carrot, chopped
Directions: Add olive oil to a soup pot and sauté onions and carrots until tender. Rinse the lentils. Add lentils and broth to the soup pot and bring to a boil. Reduce the heat to a simmer. Cover pot halfway to allow steam to get out. Let simmer until lentils are soft, about 30 minutes. Divide into 6 servings, about 1 cup per serving.

Nutrition Facts
Calories	250
Total Fat	7g
Total Carbs	34g

Snack Cranberry Almond Parfait (191 cals)
Prep Time: 5 minutes   **Total Time:** 5 minutes
Ingredients
  * 1 cup fat-free Greek yogurt   * 2 tbsp **Ayhan's Famous dried cranberries**
  * 2 tbsp sliced almonds   * 1 tbsp honey
Directions: Layer yogurt with cranberries, almonds and drizzle with honey.

Nutrition Facts
Calories	191
Total Fat	6g
Total Carbs	34g

Day 24 Meal Plan and Recipes

Breakfast — Continental Breakfast (221 cals)

Prep time: 10 minutes   **Total time:** 10 minutes

Ingredients
* 2 egg whites, hardboiled   * 1 whole grain bread, sliced and toasted
* 1 cup fat-free or soy milk, to drink   * 1/2 grapefruit   * salt and Pepper

Directions: Bring water to a boil and boil eggs for about 5 minutes. Peel and separate whites. Top toasted bread with hardboiled egg whites. Use salt, pepper to taste and enjoy. Serve with 1/2 grapefruit and glass of milk.

Nutrition Facts

Calories	221
Total Fat	1g
Saturated Fat	0g
Cholesterol	5mg
Sodium	307mg
Total Carbs	34g
Dietary Fiber	6g
Sugars	20g
Protein	20g

Lunch — Artichoke Pizza (297 cals)

Prep Time: 5 minutes   **Cook Time:** 6 minutes   **Total Time:** 11 minutes

Ingredients
* 1 whole wheat pita   * 2 tsp **Extra Virgin Olive oil**
* 1 c. **canned artichoke hearts**   * 2 oz low-fat mozzarella cheese, grated
* 1/4 tsp garlic powder   * 4 slices tomato, sliced   * salt and pepper, to taste

Directions: Cut open pita. Brush with olive oil. Bake pita for 2 minutes. Spread tomatoes, artichokes and mozzarella cheese. Sprinkle with garlic powder. Bake for additional 2-3 minutes or until cheese is melted.

Nutrition Facts

Calories	297
Total Fat	4g
Saturated Fat	2g
Cholesterol	5mg
Sodium	864mg
Total Carbs	45g
Dietary Fiber	11g
Sugars	3g
Protein	28g

Dinner — Chicken-Kebab Sandwich (420 cals)

Prep Time: 5 minutes   **Cook Time:** 15 minutes   **Total Time:** 20 minutes

Ingredients
* 4 ounces chicken breast   * 2 tbsp **Ayhan's Lite Mediterranean Vinaigrette Dressing**
* 4 large mushrooms, washed   * ½ onion, sliced   * cooking spray
* ½ whole wheat pita   * salt and pepper, to taste

Directions: Baste chicken with dressing and grill for 5-6 minutes in the oven or on a grill pan. In separate pan, sauté mushrooms and onions in cooking spray. Serve chicken in ½ pita and top with mushrooms and onions.

Nutrition Facts

Calories	420
Total Fat	16g
Saturated Fat	4g
Cholesterol	95mg
Sodium	517mg
Total Carbs	29g
Dietary Fiber	5g
Sugars	6g
Protein	40g

Dinner — Salad (237 cals)

Prep Time: 5 minutes   **Total Time:** 5 minutes

Ingredients * 2 c. salad greens   * ½ c. plum tomatoes, diced
* ½ cucumber, diced   * ¼ red onion, diced   * 8 black **olives**
* salt & pepper   * 5 tbsp **Ayhan's Lite Dressing**

Directions: Toss all ingredients with Ayhan's Lite Vinaigrette. Chill and serve.

Nutrition Facts

Calories	237
Total Fat	16g
Total Carbs	22g

Dinner — Yogurt Marinade (46 cals)

Prep Time: 5 minutes   **Total Time:** 5 minutes

Ingredients   * 3 oz fat-free yogurt
* 1 clove garlic, crushed   * 2 tsp white wine vinegar   * salt & pepper

Directions: Mix yogurt with garlic in small bowl. Add salt and pepper to taste. Before serving Chicken-Kebab Sandwich, drizzle yogurt dressing inside of pita sandwich.

Nutrition Facts

Calories	46
Total Fat	0g
Total Carbs	8g

Snack — Granola Raisin Yogurt (225 cals)

Prep Time: 2 minutes   **Total Time:** 2 minutes

Ingredients: * 1/2 cup fat free Greek yogurt
* 1/4 **cup Ayhan's Famous Granola**   * 2 tbsp raisins

Directions: Top yogurt with granola, raisins and enjoy.

Snack — 1 Apple (81 cals)

Nutrition Facts

Calories	225
Total Fat	2g
Total Carbs	45g

Day 25 Meal Plan and Recipes

Breakfast Continental Breakfast (221 cals)

Prep time: 10 minutes   **Total time:** 10 minutes

Ingredients

   * 2 egg whites, hardboiled   * 1 whole grain bread, sliced and toasted
   * 1 cup fat-free or soy milk, to drink   * 1/2 grapefruit   * salt and Pepper

Directions: Bring water to a boil and boil eggs for about 5 minutes. Peel and separate whites. Top toasted bread with hardboiled egg whites. Use salt, pepper to taste and enjoy. Serve with 1/2 grapefruit and glass of milk.

Nutrition Facts

Calories	221
Total Fat	1g
Saturated Fat	0g
Cholesterol	5mg
Sodium	307mg
Total Carbs	34g
Dietary Fiber	6g
Sugars	20g
Protein	20g

Lunch Artichoke Pizza (297 cals)

Prep Time: 5 minutes   **Cook Time:** 6 minutes   **Total Time:** 11 minutes

Ingredients

   * 1 whole wheat pita   * 2 tsp **Extra Virgin Olive oil**
   * 1 c. **canned artichoke hearts**   * 2 oz low-fat mozzarella cheese, grated
   * 1/4 tsp garlic powder   * 4 slices tomato, sliced   * salt and pepper, to taste

Directions: Cut open pita. Brush with olive oil. Bake pita for 2 minutes. Spread tomatoes, artichokes and mozzarella cheese. Sprinkle with garlic powder. Bake for additional 2-3 minutes or until cheese is melted.

Nutrition Facts

Calories	297
Total Fat	4g
Saturated Fat	2g
Cholesterol	5mg
Sodium	864mg
Total Carbs	45g
Dietary Fiber	11g
Sugars	3g
Protein	28g

Dinner Chicken-Kebab Sandwich (420 cals)

Prep Time: 5 minutes   **Cook Time:** 15 minutes   **Total Time:** 20 minutes

Ingredients

   * 4 ounces chicken breast   * 2 tbsp **Ayhan's Lite Mediterranean**
Vinaigrette Dressing
   * 4 large mushrooms, washed   * ½ onion, sliced   * cooking spray
   * ½ whole wheat pita   * salt and pepper, to taste

Directions: Baste chicken with dressing and grill for 5-6 minutes in the oven or on a grill pan. In separate pan, sauté mushrooms and onions in cooking spray. Serve chicken in ½ pita and top with mushrooms and onions.

Nutrition Facts

Calories	420
Total Fat	16g
Saturated Fat	4g
Cholesterol	95mg
Sodium	517mg
Total Carbs	29g
Dietary Fiber	5g
Sugars	6g
Protein	40g

Dinner Salad (237 cals)

Prep Time: 5 minutes   **Total Time:** 5 minutes

Ingredients   * 2 c. salad greens   * ½ c. plum tomatoes, diced
   * ½ cucumber, diced   * ¼ red onion, diced   * 8 black **olives**
   * salt & pepper   * 5 tbsp **Ayhan's Lite Dressing**

Directions: Toss all ingredients with Ayhan's Lite Vinaigrette. Chill and serve.

Nutrition Facts

Calories	237
Total Fat	16g
Total Carbs	22g

Dinner Yogurt Marinade (46 cals)

Prep Time: 5 minutes   **Total Time:** 5 minutes

Ingredients   * 3 oz fat-free yogurt
   * 1 clove garlic, crushed   * 2 tsp white wine vinegar   * salt & pepper

Directions: Mix yogurt with garlic in small bowl. Add salt and pepper to taste. Before serving Chicken-Kebab Sandwich, drizzle yogurt dressing inside of pita sandwich.

Nutrition Facts

Calories	46
Total Fat	0g
Total Carbs	8g

Snack Granola Raisin Yogurt (225 cals)

Prep Time: 2 minutes   **Total Time:** 2 minutes

Ingredients: * 1/2 cup fat free Greek yogurt
           * 1/4 **cup Ayhan's Famous Granola**   * 2 tbsp raisins

Directions: Top yogurt with granola, raisins and enjoy.

Snack 1 Apple (81 cals)

Nutrition Facts

Calories	225
Total Fat	2g
Total Carbs	45g

Ayhan's Shrimp and Chicken Kebab

Day 26 Meal Plan and Recipes

Breakfast   Apple and Cheese (179 cals)
Prep time: 2 minutes   **Total time:** 2 minutes
Ingredients
* 1 glass nonfat milk, to drink
* 2 ounces your choice of light cheese (see directions for suggestions)
* 1 granny smith apple, cut into wedges

Directions: Quick Cooking Instructions (Time: 1 minute): Purchase Laughing Cow Light Mini Babybel Cheese or Light String Cheese which are both single servings and portable. Serve apple with cheese and a glass of milk.

Nutrition Facts

Calories	179
Total Fat	15g
Saturated Fat	9g
Cholesterol	39mg
Sodium	908mg
Total Carbs	18g
Dietary Fiber	3g
Sugars	15g
Protein	20g

Lunch   Shepherd Salad (508 cals)
Prep Time: 10 minutes   **Total Time:** 10 minutes
Ingredients
* 2 cups ripe tomatoes, diced   * 1 cup Kirby cucumbers, diced
* 1/4 cup dill, chopped   * 1/4 cup red onions, diced
* 1/4 cup low-fat feta cheese, crumbled
* 4 tbsp **Ayhan's Lite Mediterranean Vinaigrette Dressing and Marinade**
* 1 whole wheat pita   * salt and pepper, to taste

Directions: Toss all ingredients with dressing. Serve with 1 whole wheat pita.

Nutrition Facts

Calories	508
Total Fat	17g
Saturated Fat	4g
Cholesterol	8mg
Sodium	1423mg
Total Carbs	58g
Dietary Fiber	9g
Sugars	20g
Protein	36g

Dinner   Broiled Flounder and Cous Cous (374 cals)
Prep Time: 10 minutes   **Cook Time:** 15 minutes **Total Time:** 25 minutes
Ingredients
* 4 ounces flounder, filet   * 3 tsp olive oil
* 1 clove garlic, sliced thin   * juice of 1/2 lemon
* 2/3 cup **flavored couscous**, cooked   * salt and pepper, to taste
* 1 tsp **Ayhan's Lemon & Herb Dressing and Marinade**

Directions: Top fish with lemon juice, olive oil, garlic, salt and pepper. Bake for 5 minutes. Prepare couscous according to package directions without added oil. When done cooking, mix in 1 tsp Lemon and Herb Dressing. Serve fish with cous cous on side.

Nutrition Facts

Calories	261
Total Fat	10g
Saturated Fat	2g
Cholesterol	43mg
Sodium	250mg
Total Carbs	13g
Dietary Fiber	5g
Sugars	5g
Protein	28g

Dinner   Sautéed Spinach (138 cals)
Prep Time: 10 minutes   **Total Time:** 10 minutes
Ingredients
* 2 ounces uncooked or 1 cup cooked **rice pilaf**

Directions: Cook according to package directions.

Nutrition Facts

Calories	138
Total Fat	14g
Total Carbs	3g

Snack   Honey Fig and Yogurt (231 cals)
Prep Time: 5 minutes   **Total Time:** 5 minutes
Ingredients
* 6 ounces of fat free Greek-style yogurt   * 1 ½ pieces of **dried figs**, sliced
* 1 tbsp honey

Directions: Top yogurt with sliced figs and drizzle with honey.

Nutrition Facts

Calories	231
Total Fat	1g
Total Carbs	49g

Snack   1 Pear (98 cals)
Prep Time: 1 minute   **Total Time:** 1 minute
Ingredients: * 1 pear

Nutrition Facts

Calories	98
Total Fat	1g
Total Carbs	25g

Ayhan's Shepherd Salad w/ Pita

Day 27 Meal Plan and Recipes

Breakfast Raspberry Cereal (259 cals)
Prep time: 5 minutes   **Total time:** 5 minutes
Ingredients
  * 3/4 cup whole grain cereal
  * 3/4 cup fresh raspberries or strawberries (sliced)
  * 1 cup fat free or soy milk
Directions: Mix cereal and berries into milk and enjoy.

Nutrition Facts
Calories	259
Total Fat	2g
Saturated Fat	0g
Cholesterol	5mg
Sodium	134mg
Total Carbs	48g
Dietary Fiber	11g
Sugars	17g
Protein	15g

Lunch Traditional Greek Salad (496 cals)
Prep Time: 10 minutes   **Total Time:** 10 minutes
Ingredients
  * 3 cups salad greens   * 1/4 cup scallions, chopped
  * 1/4 cup carrots, shredded   * 1/4 cup red cabbage, diced
  * 2 tbsp dill, chopped   * 3 ounces low-fat feta cheese
  * 8 **kalamata olives**   * 1/2 whole wheat pita
  * 3 tbsp **Ayhan's Mediterranean Vinaigrette Dressing and Marinade**
Directions: Toss all vegetables with Ayhan's Vinaigrette Dressing and serve with 1/2 whole wheat pita.

Nutrition Facts
Calories	496
Total Fat	30g
Saturated Fat	7g
Cholesterol	18mg
Sodium	1245mg
Total Carbs	34g
Dietary Fiber	8g
Sugars	7g
Protein	27g

Dinner Scallops Mediterranean (578 cals)
Prep Time: 5 minutes   **Cook Time:** 15 minutes   **Total Time:** 20 minutes
Ingredients
  * 4 ounces scallops, sea or bay   * 1/4 cup sun dried tomatoes, diced
  * 1 tsp tomato paste   * 1 tsp dill, chopped   * 4 tbsp water
  * 1 clove garlic, diced   * 3 tbsp **Ayhan's Lemon & Herb Dressing and Marinade**
  * 1 cup long grain rice, cooked
Directions: Place scallops in casserole or baking pan. In separate bowl, mix tomato paste with remaining ingredients (except rice). Pour mixture over scallops and bake at 450 degrees until tender, about 10 minutes. Prepare rice according to package directions, without adding any oil or butter. Place scallops over rice and drizzle remaining liquid over the top.

Nutrition Facts
Calories	578
Total Fat	22g
Saturated Fat	4g
Cholesterol	28mg
Sodium	1139mg
Total Carbs	74g
Dietary Fiber	9g
Sugars	7g
Protein	26g

Snack Raisin Granola (130 cals)
Prep Time: 2 minutes   **Total Time:** 2 minutes
Ingredients
  * 1/4 cup **Ayhan's Famous Granola** (any variety)   * 2 tbsp golden raisins
Directions: Mix granola with raisins and serve.

Nutrition Facts
Calories	130
Total Fat	1g
Saturated Fat	0g
Cholesterol	0mg
Sodium	49mg
Total Carbs	31g
Dietary Fiber	2g
Sugars	18g
Protein	2g

Snack Orange & Yogurt (167 cals)
Prep Time: 2 minutes   **Total Time:** 2 minutes
Ingredients:
  * 1 orange   * 6 ounces "lite", 90 calorie yogurt
Directions: Peel and separate orange, serve on top of yogurt.

Nutrition Facts
Calories	167
Total Fat	0g
Total Carbs	30g

Day 28 Meal Plan and Recipes

Breakfast — Toast with Cream Cheese & Jam (281 cals)

Prep time: 5 minutes   **Total time:** 5 minutes

Ingredients
* 2 slices 100 % whole wheat toast
* 1 tbsp **Hai Orange Jam** or any all fruit spread
* 2 tbsp fat free cream cheese

Directions: Spread jam on one slice of toast and spread cream cheese on the other. Serve as a sandwich.

Nutrition Facts	
Calories	281
Total Fat	9g
Saturated Fat	5g
Cholesterol	22mg
Sodium	449mg
Total Carbs	43g
Dietary Fiber	3g
Sugars	16g
Protein	9g

Lunch — Spinach Pie (466 cals)

Prep Time: 10 minutes **Cook Time:** 15 minutes   **Total Time:** 10 minutes

Ingredients
* 2 sheets phyllo dough
* 2 ounces low-fat feta cheese, crumbled
* 2 cup spinach, fresh or frozen
* 2 tbsp olive oil
* as needed cooking spray
* 1 clove and garlic, crushed
* 1 tbsp low fat parmesan cheese, grated
* ¼ cup onions, diced
* 2 egg white
* 1 cup fat free or soy milk, to drink
* to taste salt and pepper

Directions: Steam the spinach either in the microwave or on the stovetop, squeeze out any water, and set aside. Sauté onions with garlic with 1 tbsp olive oil until soft. Add spinach and sauté 5 minutes. Allow to cool. Add cheeses, egg whites, and salt and pepper, to taste. Brush phyllo dough with remaining oil. Spread ingredients between 2 pieces of phyllo and fold into triangular shape. Spray cooking sheet with cooking spray to avoid sticking. Bake at 450 degrees for 10 minutes, until golden brown.

Nutrition Facts	
Calories	466
Total Fat	33g
Saturated Fat	5g
Cholesterol	15mg
Sodium	360mg
Total Carbs	28g
Dietary Fiber	2g
Sugars	7g
Protein	20g

Dinner — Tilapia Mediterranean with Basmati Rice (454 cals)

Prep Time: 5 minutes   **Cook Time:** 15 minutes   **Total Time:** 20 minutes

Ingredients
* 4 ounces tilapia fish filet   * 3 tsp olive oil   * 1 garlic clove, sliced
* juice of 1 fresh lemon   * 2/3 cup **basmati rice**, cooked   * 1 cup broccoli
* 1/4 cup water   * 1 tbsp **Krinos capers**   * salt and pepper to taste

Directions: Sautee garlic in olive oil until golden brown. Place fish in saucepan and top with sautéed garlic, capers, water, lemon juice, salt and pepper to taste. Cover and simmer for 15 minutes. Steam broccoli until desired tenderness. Prepare basmati rice according to package directions. Serve fish with 2/3 cup basmati rice and broccoli spears.

Nutrition Facts	
Calories	454
Total Fat	17g
Saturated Fat	2g
Cholesterol	54mg
Sodium	135mg
Total Carbs	70g
Dietary Fiber	8g
Sugars	17g
Protein	31g

Snack — Banana and Walnut Yogurt (330 cals)

Prep Time: 2 minutes   **Total Time:** 2 minutes

Ingredients   * 6 oz plain, fat free yogurt   * 1 small banana   * 10-12 **walnut halves**

Directions: Top yogurt with sliced banana and walnuts.

Snack — Pineapple Chunks (60 cals)

Prep Time: 1 minute   **Total Time:** 1 minute

Ingredients: * ¾ cup pineapple chunks (fresh, or in natural or lite juices)

Directions: Eat and enjoy.

Nutrition Facts	
Calories	330
Total Fat	11g
Saturated Fat	2g
Cholesterol	11mg
Sodium	114mg
Total Carbs	50g
Dietary Fiber	4g
Sugars	37g
Protein	12g

Keeping it off with the Anti-Aging Maintenance Program

The first step in maintaining your weight and health is to continue enjoying the wonderful meals provided in Ayhan's Mediterranean Menu Plans® weekly regimens. Ayhan has supplemented this strong foundation for maintaining ahealthy body by partnering with the leading fitness expert, Liz Gillies, to create a time saving workout program to keep your body in top condition. You may be familiar with Liz's pioneering Pilate's and Stability Ball programs.

Her Anti-Aging program is designed to support an active lifestyle for people forty five or older and grant long term health benefits.

As remarked upon earlier, the Mediterranean diet can help prevent Alzheimer's, breast and prostate cancer, diabetes, gallstones, and hypertension. It also helps with combating inflammation of cells that may lead to disease and lowering cholesterol. The Anti-Aging program focuses on each of these and supplements the Mediterranean diet's already significant ability in reducing the likelihood of heart disorders. You cannot forget the all-important Vitamin E available in all Ayhan's Mediterranean meals in enhancing the length and quality of your life. The health benefits alone make Ayhan's Mediterranean Menu Plans® Diet one of the foremost diets in the world!

How you can start your own healthy Diet plan

Thousands of people have enjoyed Ayhan's diet recipes. The benefits of Ayhan's Mediterranean Menu Plans® speak for themselves. This diet has much to offer, including customized plans for fast, healthy weight loss, maintaining your weight with great tasting food, easy recipes and convenient online ordering. Now you can start to enjoy the benefits with the easy online form that makes Ayhan's Mediterranean Menu Plans® Diet available to you immediately.

Research Studies

The cuisine known as the "Mediterranean Diet" has been called "The Healthiest Diet in the World". It has been popular in Greece, Cyprus, Turkey, southern Italy and nearby regions for centuries. The "Mediterranean Diet" is low in saturated fat and provides healthy mono-unsaturated fats from olive oil, fish and nuts. It features yogurt and smaller portions of meats and the heart healthy benefits of wine. The Diet is also high in fiber from whole grains, dried fruits and vegetables. In recent years many scientific studies have shown that people who follow this way of eating enjoy better health and longer lives than those who consume a western European style diet.

Scientific studies have shown that the Mediterranean Diet:

- helps prevent heart attacks and cardiovascular disease
- protects against breast cancer and prostate cancer
- helps prevent gallstones
- reduces high blood pressure and cholesterol
- significantly increases life span
- effective in reducing the risk factors of Metabolic Syndrome
- study shows 40% reduction in the rate of Alzheimers disease
- helps protects against ALS (Lou Gehrig disease)
- shown to reduce birth defects like spina bifida

The results are so significant that newspapers across the country have been touting the incredible research analysis from many clinical studies measuring the effects of the Mediterranean diet with respect to health and weight loss. The spectacular findings have reinforced the growing understanding that the Mediterranean diet is the best diet today.

The People Behind 28 Day Ayhan's Mediterranean Diet Plan®

Ayhan, The Chef and Mediterranean Food Guru

Ayhan was born in Cyprus, an island in the Mediterranean south of Turkey. As a young man he moved to the United States and soon became a Long Island restaurateur. He excelled in the restaurant business and founded the leading group of restaurants specializing in Mediterranean fare. His dedication to his craft led him to visits various countries along the Mediterranean shores searching for high quality ingredients to add to his growing list of award winning recipes. His success in the restaurant industry resulted in his own brand of salad dressing, which is sold in hundreds of supermarkets and online at www.amazon.com

Ayhan's desire to provide the benefits of his healthy restaurant recipes and fine ingredients to everyone as easily as possible led to the development of the online Ayhan's Mediterranean Menu Plans® diet plan at www.amdiets.com and to the launching of the online marketplace at www.ayhans.com.

Debra, The Nutritionist

Debra Grossano, MS, RD, CDN, CDE, has been a registered dietician for over 5 years and has a well established practice in Manhattan. She has an undergraduate degree from Rutgers University and a Master's Degree in clinical Nutrition from New York University. Debra has worked as a specialist in corporate fitness and was heavily involved with personal fitness and promoting health in the workplace. She is a leading expert on proper analysis of nutritional content and portion control in successful dieting. Debbie is also a Certified Diabetes Educator.

Christopher, The Strategist

Christopher Speed, MND, APD has a Master Degree of Human Nutrition from the University of Sydney. Christopher is the author of several important articles about the Mediterranean diet. He continues his professional interest in nutrition and self care as an associate editor of the European Journal of Cancer Prevention and as a nutrition consultant to major corporations in New York City.

**Visit www.amdiets.com
to view the Mediterranean Diet Plan online!**

Some of our Biggest Fans

Ayhan's Mediterranean Menu Plans® Diet has garnered many supporters worldwide:

Dr. Sinan Berkay, a heart specialist who lives and works in Long Island, recommends Ayhan's Diet to all his patients to enhance the quality of their life and promote longevity.

Dr. Ergun Birinci, a practicing General Surgeon in Europe, is an active supporter of Ayhan's Mediterranean Diet as a key to healthy living.

Dr. Andrew Siegel, a leading Urologist at the famous Hackensack Medical Center in New Jersey, endorses Ayhan's diet and also Ayhan's All Natural Mediterranean Salad Dressings.

Vijay B. Vad, MD specializes in Sports Medicine and has been a major endorser of Ayhan's Mediterranean Menu Plans® Diet. The well balanced meals offered under the diet are ideal for athletes that want a nutritional meal that meets their energy needs, while helping keep them in top shape.

Vijay B. Vad, MD

Some Other Reading Material

The Mediterranean diet has spawned ample material for you to research to learn more about the amazing health and diet benefits using the diet will give you. There are also cookbooks available that can help you explore the cuisine when you reach the Maintenance mode. These, along with Ayhan's collection of free recipes available online, will provide you guidance to keep living healthy!

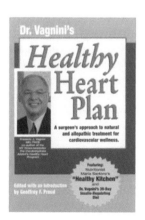

Notes

Notes

LaVergne, TN USA
13 May 2010
1790LVUK00005B